MAPPING
THE OCEANS

MAPPING
THE OCEANS

Discovering the world beneath our seas

Carolyn Fry

ARCTURUS

For my nieces and nephews:
Alex, Matthew and Kathryn Bland and
Annabel, Grace and Imogen Deffee

Acknowledgements

The author would like to thank Dr Megan Barford, Map Curator at Royal Museums Greenwich for her helpful comments on the manuscript; Vanessa Daubney, John Turing and other staff at Arcturus Publishing for turning the manuscript into this vibrant, illustrated book; Jackie Deffee for assistance with early research; and staff at both the Caird Library and Archive at the National Maritime Museum in Greenwich and the National Oceanographic Library of the National Oceanography Centre in Southampton.

In association with Royal Museums Greenwich

At the heart of the UNESCO World Heritage Site of Maritime Greenwich are the four world-class attractions of Royal Museums Greenwich – the National Maritime Museum, *Cutty Sark*, the Royal Observatory, and the Queen's House.

ARCTURUS

This edition published in 2020 by Arcturus Publishing Limited
26/27 Bickels Yard, 151–153 Bermondsey Street,
London SE1 3HA

ISBN: 978-1-78828-092-1
AD005828UK

Printed in Singapore

CONTENTS

INTRODUCTION

Explaining how humans have sought to explore, record and understand the oceans that cover 71% of Earth is no easy task, particularly in just 192 pages. It is a story that spans at least 65,000 years, from the arrival by sea of early humans on primitive craft to Australia, to the first-ever dive to the world's deepest known point in 1960 and current efforts to understand the global impacts of climate change. This book is therefore very much 'a' history of mapping the oceans rather than 'the' history.

I interpret the term 'mapping' quite loosely in the book; it is not simply a technical book about hydrography. Rather, I explore characters and events that have been instrumental in advancing many aspects of our understanding of the oceans. This means I touch on everything from how humans first learned to survive, sail and navigate the oceans; to advances in boat building; and the emergence and evolution of oceanography as a scientific discipline.

The book runs roughly chronologically. The first chapter examines several events that we know happened but for which there is scant evidence. The earliest crossing to Australia is one example, as are the colonization of Easter Island across a vast stretch of ocean, and the development of the first sailing vessels by ancient Egyptians. By the chapter's end, the Phoenicians and Greeks have embraced sailing as a means to trade, and the Vikings have used it to conquer new lands.

Chapter 2 tells of some magnificent exploration achievements, including voyages by the Chinese as far as Africa, as a demonstration of wealth and power, and those of empire-building Europeans with aims to dominate trading routes and colonize lands they encountered. It also investigates the means by which sailing was slowly made safer; the invention of the compass and sailors' use of portolan charts are two examples.

The start of Chapter 3 finds seafarers suffering from being unable to calculate longitude. Solving this issue contributed to Captain James Cook being able to dismiss the long-standing European notion of a habitable southern continent. With the world's landmasses and oceans now positioned with relatively accuracy, naturalists could focus on filling in the details of coastal areas and studying the characteristics of oceans. The findings of some such scientific investigations, such as Charles Darwin's examination of coral reefs and the three-year *Challenger* expedition, are presented in Chapter 4.

In Chapters 5 and 6, new technologies contribute greatly to driving ocean science forward. We learn that the invention of echo-sounding, advances in diving technology and the emergence of satellite imaging have been fundamental to scientists learning more about the physical processes at work in the oceans, the atmosphere and on land. Critically, they have helped to reveal that recent human activity has had an enormous impact on marine ecosystems that must be urgently addressed.

Having researched the long history of humans' remarkable efforts to map the world's oceans, I find the most extraordinary thing is how little we have

Above: *A world map produced by John Blaeu c. 1662. For centuries, people have sought to more accurately chart the oceans that make up most of the planet's surface.*

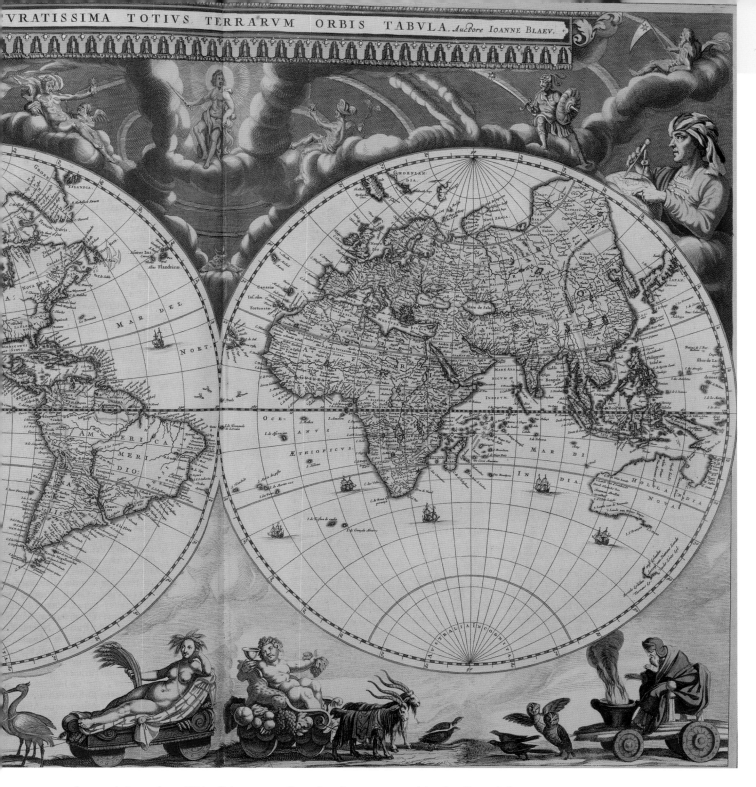

learned. Less than 18% of the ocean floor has been mapped in detail, and there are huge gaps in our knowledge of marine life. It is down to new generations of dedicated seafaring pioneers, armed with autonomous seafaring robots and other innovative technologies, to address these deficiencies and ensure we manage our oceans better in the coming centuries and millennia.

Carolyn Fry

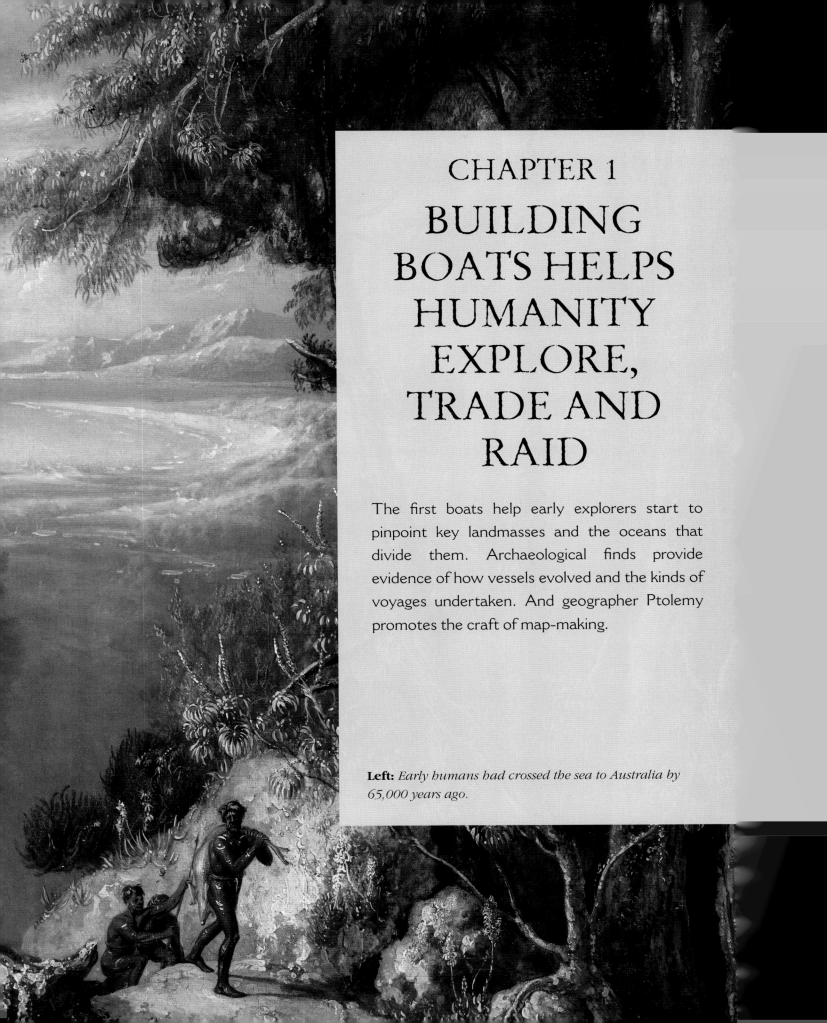

CHAPTER 1
BUILDING BOATS HELPS HUMANITY EXPLORE, TRADE AND RAID

The first boats help early explorers start to pinpoint key landmasses and the oceans that divide them. Archaeological finds provide evidence of how vessels evolved and the kinds of voyages undertaken. And geographer Ptolemy promotes the craft of map-making.

Left: *Early humans had crossed the sea to Australia by 65,000 years ago.*

THE EARLIEST SEAFARERS EXPLOIT LOWER SEA LEVELS

The blue of the oceans dominates Earth; dry land constitutes a mere 29 per cent of its cover. When our hominid ancestors evolved from forest-dwelling primates and began spreading out across the African savannahs around seven million years ago (mya), it was inevitable that they would soon reach coastal areas. Those who did, discovered a rich larder of marine plants and creatures in the shallow waters bounding the land.

Descendants of these pioneers may have used hollowed-out logs or bamboo rafts to traverse small bodies of water as they exploited this food source. Eventually, some would, through choice or accident, have made their way into deeper waters, perhaps to offshore islands they could see from their home shores. It was then only a matter of time before some travelled far enough by sea that their homeland became lost to the horizon a few kilometres behind them.

Recent archaeological research suggests that the first long-term seafaring took place in Southeast Asia at least as far back as 65,000 years ago. This was during the Pleistocene, the geological epoch between 2.58 mya and 11,700 years ago. During this period, ice repeatedly advanced and retreated from the Earth's poles. The ice age between 71,000 and 59,000 years ago locked up water in glaciers, lowering the sea level; 65,000 years ago it was around 85 m (280 ft) lower than today. This shortened the distances between landmasses, aiding early seaborne pioneers.

If you were to roll back the sea from the southeast of the Malay Peninsula, around Sumatra, Borneo, Java, Madura, Bali and surrounding islands, you would reveal the Sunda Shelf. It was from this now submerged land that archaeologists believe the earliest seafarers travelled. Their craft and survival skills must have been sufficient to carry them some 90 km (56 miles) across the sea to reach the then exposed Sahul Shelf, which today extends northwest from Australia beneath the waves.

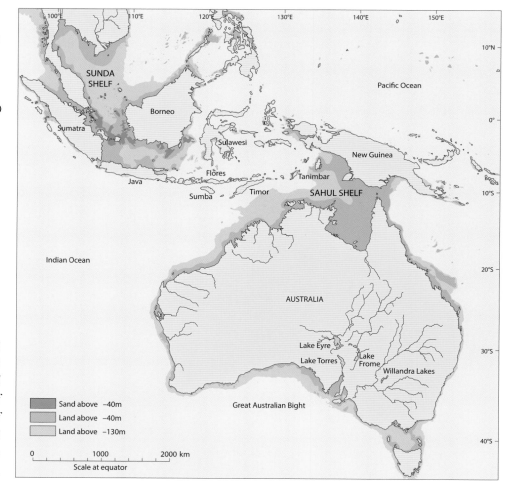

Right: *Map showing seafloor depths of the Sunda Shelf in Southeast Asia and the Sahul Shelf north of Australia. The Sahul Shelf would have been exposed during lower sea levels 65,000 years ago.*

No boats dating back to such far-off times have ever been found, but archaeological sites give us clues as to when our ancestors first made the crossing. The site that has provided the date of 65,000 years ago is an Aboriginal rock shelter called Madjedbebe, which lies around 50 km (30 miles) from the coast in the Northern Territory. It has yielded thousands of artefacts, including an ancient campfire, mortars and pestles, flaked stone tools and wall decorations made using ochre. Human activity at another nearby site, Nauwalabila I, has been dated to between 53,000 and 60,000 years old. The subsequent rise of the sea level may well have submerged other sites inhabited by the first inhabitants of Australia.

Some scientists are sceptical that humans made it so far across water, so early. However, it is clear that the wider colonization of the Australian continent was in progress by around 48,000–50,000 years ago. Studies of maternal genetic lineages show that Aboriginal people spread out during this time from the north, travelling the coastline in both easterly and westerly directions. Their paths crossed in the south, just west of modern-day Adelaide. Meanwhile, the dates of a plethora of archaeological sites around the continent's current coastline tally with the genetic dates. One, a remote island cave located off northwest Australia, was inhabited between 50,000 and 30,000 years ago.

Right: *There is much evidence to show that humans were colonizing Australia by 48,000–50,000 BCE. This rock painting at Ubirr in Kakadu National Park is 30,000 years old.*

The first crossing to Australia

Two main hypotheses have been put forward about the route taken by Australia's first inhabitants. One favours a route through northern Indonesia to New Guinea (which was joined to Australia, as part of the exposed Sahul landmass at that time). The other supports a more southerly route, across Sumatra and Java and onwards to Timor (the southeasterly extent of the Sunda landmass) and then to Sahul.

An early argument for the more northerly route was that the islands of northern Indonesia are close together and the early seafarers would therefore have been able to see the landmass that now forms New Guinea before setting out for it. The assumption was that the terrain which now forms Australia would not have been visible from any Indonesian island, making the journey via this route less likely.

However, research published in 2018 used computer analyses incorporating historic sea levels, landscape surface height and ocean-floor data to show how far people at the time could see from any location in Southeast Asia. The scientists concluded that early seafarers on the Indonesian islands of Timor and Rote were able to see a now-submerged island chain – the Sahul Banks – stretching for some 700 km (435 miles) in the Timor Sea. And from here, the Australian part of Sahul was visible.

Above: *The first humans in Australia may have travelled from the Timor coastline, seen here, via a now-submerged island chain.*

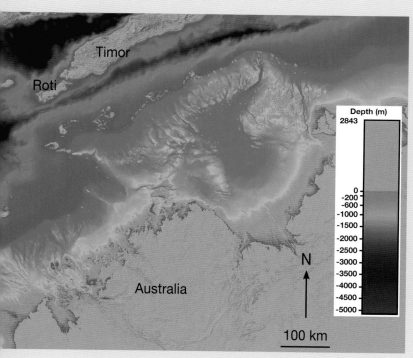

Depth (m)
2843

0
-200
-600
-1000
-1500
-2000
-2500
-3000
-3500
-4000
-4500
-5000

N

100 km

Above: *This image depicting ocean depth off of northwestern Australia shows the now submerged Sahul Banks.*

Crossing from this island chain brought the mariners to the now submerged coastline, close to where the oldest archaeological sites of Madjedbebe and Nauwalabila I are located. Entering via New Guinea would have required considerable additional travel to reach these sites.

Planned and purposeful

The findings of research combining voyage simulations and population genetics, meanwhile, have led a team of Australian scientists to conclude that the first marine voyages were 'planned and purposeful'. The team simulated voyages during the summer monsoon (when north-to-northwesterly winds maximized mariners' chances). The findings revealed that accidental drifting was unlikely to bring vessels to Sahul, while modest paddling towards the Sahul Banks from Timor and Rote was likely to result in success.

The genetics research suggested that at least 72 individuals and perhaps as many as 100 were needed for successful colonization of Sahul, lending support to the idea that the first mariners arrived through choice, not chance.

POLYNESIA'S MASTERS OF LONG-DISTANCE NAVIGATION

Within the triangle linking the Hawaiian Islands, New Zealand and Easter Island lie more than 1,000 islands. These, together with the island group of Tuvalu, and enclaves in the Solomon Islands and Vanuatu, make up Polynesia. Language, culture and beliefs link these islands' disparate inhabitants.

Colonization of Polynesia began during the lower sea levels of the Pleistocene, when people from Southeast Asia began moving from island to island along the coast. Radiocarbon dating of a rock shelter indicates that humans had settled in the Solomon Islands by around 26,000 BCE.

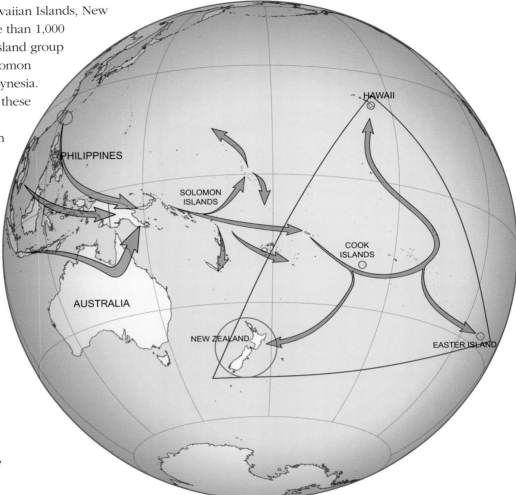

Right: *Two waves of settlers populated Polynesia. The earliest (blue arrows) had reached the Solomon Islands by 26,000 BCE. Later settlers arrived much later (pink arrows), reaching Hawaii and Easter Island in 900 and the Cook Islands in 700.*

Some 25,000 years later a new wave of pioneers, originating in southern China and defined by Lapita ceramics, spread southeast from the Solomon Islands to the Santa Cruz Islands, Vanuatu, the Loyalty Islands and New Caledonia. Some crossed 830 km (450 nautical miles) of ocean to reach Fiji, arriving *c.* 1000 BCE. (One nautical mile is equal to one minute of latitude or 1.1508 land-measured miles.)

Left: *Later settlers in Polynesia were characterised by Lapita ceramics, such as depicted in this plaster cast.*

The descendants of these people colonized Samoa around 800 BCE. Around 1,900 years passed before the central Society Islands became inhabited. Then a period of rapid dispersal within a couple of centuries resulted in the colonization of New Zealand, Hawaii and Easter Island – the furthest reaches of the Polynesian triangle. Easter Island lies more than 1,610 km (1,000 miles) from Pitcairn, its closest island neighbour.

Experts have long pondered how these early people had the technology and skills to build seaworthy craft and propel them across vast stretches of ocean to reach relatively small island targets. With little archaeological evidence available, they have looked for clues in descriptions of boats written by the first European explorers to Polynesia in the eighteenth century.

Joseph Banks, a botanist on board Captain Cook's circumnavigation of the world between 1768 and 1771, described boats used to travel between islands around Tahiti and Tonga as being 30–60 ft (9–18 m) long and narrow, with either two hulls lashed together or a single hull with outrigger, propelled by both paddles and sails. Groups crowded on to such vessels to make the journeys. These sailors navigated using the stars, sun and wave patterns, with high volcanic island peaks as reference points. The flight paths of birds also gave indications of land.

Opposite: *It is possible that early settlers to Polynesia travelled in doubled-hulled canoes, such as that depicted here from c.1790 in Tonga.*

Above: *When Captain James Cook visited Polynesia between 1768 and 1771, expedition botanist Joseph Banks recorded the types of vessels used by locals to travel between islands.*

In the Marshall Islands, which lie within the island group of Micronesia to the west of Polynesia, sailors historically created navigational charts using sticks and shells to illustrate interactions between the sea and land. Shells represented islands, curved sticks showed where land deflected ocean swells, and straight sticks indicated currents near islands. It is possible that Polynesia's early sailors used similar technologies and navigational methods.

Whatever techniques Polynesia's early seafarers used, we know they were not simply carried to islands by the wind and currents. This is because the pattern of colonization largely conforms with sailors travelling against the prevailing wind direction to reach each new destination. This suggests that they waited for the prevailing wind direction to shift before setting out, the idea being that, if need be, they would be able to return home when the wind direction switched back again.

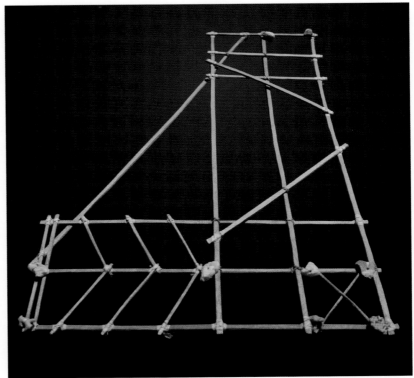

Above: *A navigational chart from the Marshall Islands, with sticks and shells used to represent local ocean characteristics.*

A major change in wind patterns, identified in research published in 2014 by scientists at Macquarie University in Sydney, Australia, may explain the surprisingly rapid colonization of Hawaii, New Zealand and Easter Island. Today, winds blow east to west in the Tropics and the opposite way farther south. This situation would have made it a struggle for early seafarers to sail either east to Easter Island or west to New Zealand, particularly since there is no evidence to suggest they used fixed-mast canoes that could have coped with such winds.

However, from evidence stored in tree rings, lake sediments and ice cores, the scientists deduced that between 1080 and 1100 the Tropics contracted. This moved westerly winds farther north, making an eastwards journey to Easter Island more viable. Then between 1140 and 1160 the opposite occurred, sending easterly winds farther south – and assisting a journey to New Zealand. These wind changes stopped as abruptly as they had started, which may be why no major voyages appear to have taken place after 1300.

Opposite: *Fishing has provided food for ancient Egyptians for many thousands of years. This scene from the tomb of the administrator Menna, dated to 1400–1352 BCE, depicts hunting for fish from a papyrus skiff.*

Below: *A shift in wind patterns may have helped early settlers to make the journey to Easter Island. Its nearest neighbour, Pitcairn, lies more than 1,610 km (1000 miles) away.*

ANCIENT EGYPTIANS MASTER BOAT BUILDING AND SAILING

As with the early Polynesian seafarers, we have only circumstantial clues about the earliest use of boats by the ancient Egyptians. Evidence from between 30,000 and 10,000 BCE indicates that hunter-gatherers inhabiting the Nile Valley fished shallow-water species from the flood plain. This could have been carried out from the shore, but may also have involved simple rafts made from the papyrus sedge *Cyperus papyrus*.

From around 10,000 to 8000 BCE, there is evidence for a wider range of fish species being caught, including those dwelling in the main Nile channel. Technological advances, including nets, fish hooks and improved vessels, made it possible for the ancient Egyptians to catch a wider range of fish than their predecessors, from the deeper water of the channel. Fish, which could be dried and kept for later consumption, continued to be important as peripatetic hunter-gathering gave way to sedentary farming at around 8000 BCE.

The Nile environment proved highly conducive for the development of water-borne transport by the early settled communities. Thanks to an image carved on to a granite pebble, we know that the Egyptians were capable of building boats with a steering system and cabin as far back as 7000 BCE. The image of the first vessel with a sail also hails from the Nile; it appears on an earthenware pot from Naqada dating to 3300–3100 BCE. The Nile flows northward towards the Mediterranean, making paddling in this direction easy. However, the prevailing wind direction is from the north. A following wind would have aided paddling against the current to a certain extent, but a sail reduced the effort considerably.

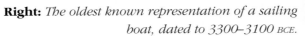

Right: *The oldest known representation of a sailing boat, dated to 3300–3100 BCE.*

Types of boats progressed from small, basic papyrus rafts to larger vessels with upturned ends secured by stays to a pole. When the Egyptians also began to make boats from wood, most likely after the development of copper tools around 3500 BCE, they retained the raised prow and stern shape of the papyrus craft. The boat with a sail depicted on the Naqada jar was likely fashioned from wood, as it had a single mast pole. Experts believe a single pole would have exerted too much downward pressure on a reed boat, causing the pole to penetrate the hull.

In 1954, archaeologists learned much of the technical sophistication with which the ancient Egyptians were able to build wooden boats, when a 44 m (144 ft) long, disassembled vessel was discovered behind a wall at the base of the Great Pyramid at Giza. Some 4,500 years old, the boat had been entombed as part of the funeral rites of the Egyptian pharaoh Khufu. In the decades following its discovery, more than 1,200 pieces of wood, mostly cedar, were recovered and the boat reconstructed. Its presence in a royal tomb clearly indicates the importance of boats and ships to ancient Egyptian civilization.

We know from the *Pyramid Texts*, a collection of ancient religious texts written on tomb walls, that by 2400–2300 BCE the Egyptians were building more than 30 kinds of vessels; in total, ancient Egyptian sources record the existence of more than 100 types. As well as being important in religious ceremonies, boats and ships were used for fishing, hunting, military uses and transporting passengers and cargoes. The construction of pyramids and other monuments was possible only because the ancient Egyptians were able to ship thousand-ton stone blocks hundreds of kilometres from quarries to where they were needed.

Above: *Texts inscribed on the Palermo Stone suggest that long-distance journeys were made by ship as far back as 2613 BCE.*

The ancient Egyptians' mastery of boat building and sailing, combined with their close proximity to the Mediterranean and Red Seas, presented opportunities for trading farther afield. The Palermo stone (part of a stele documenting significant events between the first and fifth dynasties) hints at this, describing '40 boats filled with cedar wood' being brought (from Lebanon) during King Snefuru's reign (around 2613–2589 BCE). And scenes carved in around 1480 BCE on Queen Hatshepsut's temple at Deir-el Bahri depict a sea voyage to the land of 'Punt' (likely to be somewhere southeast of Egypt on Africa's east coast) to obtain live myrrh trees and other costly and precious materials.

It was only in 2004 that indisputable evidence for ancient Egyptian seafaring emerged, however. Archaeologists investigating a dried-up lagoon on the Red Sea shore at Mersa Gawasis encountered a cave containing: broken boxes made from cedar planks; wood chips; shattered storage jars; stone anchors; and a piece of pottery inscribed with the name of Amenemhat II, a pharaoh who ruled around 1800 BCE. Subsequent investigations revealed

Opposite: *Very well preserved, the Khufu ship demonstrates the importance of seafaring in ancient Egypt.*

Above: *Scenes from Queen Hatshepsut's temple depicting a major expedition to Punt.*

seven more caves, containing timbers and oars similar to those depicted in Hatshepsut's wall carvings. There were also stone inscriptions that mentioned trips to Punt. Two sycamore planks were marked with directions for assembling a ship. Many of the artefacts were punctuated with holes made by saltwater shipworms, confirming their use at sea.

The closest shipyards to the site were at Qena, a city on the Nile some 160 km (100 miles) across the desert. The archaeologists who unearthed the caves believe that the ancient Egyptians carried disassembled boats from Qena to Mersa Gawasis before assembling them and setting off across the Red Sea to Punt. They returned via the same route, a round journey of four months involving thousands of men. It is known that for most of Egypt's ancient history, wares from Punt travelled on overland caravan routes. However, around the time that Mersa Gawasis came into use, a hostile new kingdom arose in the south, cutting Egypt off from its regular trade link. It is possible that this is what first motivated the ancient Egyptians to set sail on the high seas, as far back as 3,500 years ago.

PHOENICIANS AND ANCIENT GREEKS UNDERPIN TRADING WITH SAILING

Phoenician sailors move goods across the Mediterranean

The Egyptians may have invented the sail, but it was the Phoenicians who mastered its use for trading. At around the same time as Hatshepsut was making the first import of live trees from Punt (1493 BCE), the Phoenician civilization was in its ascendency. Hailing from lands north of present-day Israel, the Phoenicians had earlier established the major coastal city-states of Sidon and Tyre (south of modern-day Beirut, Lebanon) and Byblos (north of Beirut). Then, from 1200 BCE, they used their maritime prowess to spread out across the Mediterranean from their coastal strongholds.

The Phoenicians were driven by a desire to find new commodities and markets. Widespread trading had taken place across the Mediterranean in earlier times, but the Phoenicians were the first culture to use trade as a route to colonization. Over four centuries they established 60 city-states in the western Mediterranean, including Leptis Magna (in modern-day Libya), Carthage on the coast of North Africa, Cádiz (in Spain) and Palermo (in Italy). These settlements started out as trading posts but became more established over time, eventually becoming colonies and cities with permanent populations.

Below: *This map of Phoenician trade routes around the Mediterranean shows that not all journeys followed the coastline.*

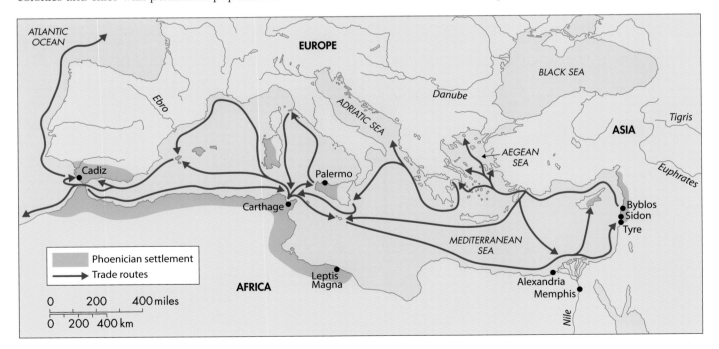

The Phoenicians sailed the Mediterranean in oar-powered sailing galleys, trading goods including slaves, glass, wine, gold, oil, ceramics, purple dye (made from the shells of murex snails), silver and tin. The scant evidence available of their trading activities comes largely from artworks and shipwrecks. Items recovered from an assemblage of three shipwrecks at Bajo de la Campana off the coast of Spain and dated to 700–600 BCE, include a stone altar, elephant tusks (most likely from Africa), ingots of tin and copper, lead ore nuggets, pottery from Andalusia, raw amber (from the Baltic) and pine nuts. This highlights the diversity of goods traded and the extent of Phoenician trading networks.

Below: *The Spanish city of Cádiz was founded by the Phoenicians in 1110 BCE.*

The oldest known Phoenician wreck, dating to 700 BCE, was discovered in 2007, west of the Maltese island of Gozo. The wreck contained grinding stones made from volcanic rock, along with dozens of urns and amphorae of a type not encountered before. Testing revealed that some of the ceramics had once contained local honey. The site was documented by archaeologists from the University of Malta, who believe the ship was following a central Mediterranean route, loading and unloading goods at ports along the way. It probably met its fate after receiving a cargo of local Gozitan products and heading for North Africa. In time, the archaeologists hope to sample wood from the hull of the ship to learn more about the craft's provenance.

Left: *Metalware was one of many goods traded by the Phoenicians.*

The start of seafaring in the Mediterranean

The earliest evidence for seafaring in the Mediterranean comes from obsidian, a volcanic glass that was used in prehistory to make chipped stone tools. Obsidian dating from 11,000 BCE and found on mainland Greece can be traced, through scientific fingerprinting, to the islands of Melos, Giali and Antiparos in the Aegean Sea and those of Lipari, Pantelleria, Palmarola and Sardinia, to the west and southwest of Italy. Scientists believe that, for 4,500 years from 6000 BCE, obsidian was regularly transported hundreds of kilometres in the Mediterranean region. This could have been achieved only by seaworthy vessels and competent navigators.

Right: *Obsidian, such as this from the Greek island of Melos, provides clues to early seafaring capabilities.*

The Greeks produce the first guides to coastal areas

Between 800 and 600 BCE, the Greek civilization followed a similar trajectory to that of the Phoenicians, establishing colonies and trading stations in the central and western Mediterranean, and also along the Dardanelles waterway (between the Aegean Sea and the Sea of Marmara) and around the Black Sea. However, the Greeks were motivated less by commercial desires and more by overpopulation at home. The two cultures were largely peaceable, but competition occasionally led to conflict.

The prosperity of both the Phoenicians and the Greeks was reliant on their ability to shift large volumes of goods across long distances. With the sea often providing the best opportunity for fast and relatively safe transportation, shipping technology evolved during this period. Two major types of ships are known to have been used by both the Phoenicians and Greeks: merchant ships, with wide, rounded hulls and a large cargo-carrying capacity; and sleeker warships with pointed rams extending from their bows. Both types were powered by a combination of sails and banks of rowers.

Above: Olympias, *a reconstruction of a trireme warship of the kind used by Phoenicians and Greeks.*

Left: *Pytheas travelled from southern France around Britain in 320 BCE, recording details of Atlantic life.*

Phoenician and Greek sailors were guided by natural and human-made landmarks, the sun and stars, and clues from currents, swells, clouds and winds. The mountainous coastline around the Mediterranean meant that, like sailors today, they could often venture into deep waters away from the shore without losing sight of land. However, Homer's poem *Odyssey*, dating back to the beginnings of Western literature some 700 years BCE, describes several open sea voyages.

The Greek historian Herodotus reports a particularly audacious journey: the three-year circumnavigation of Africa by Phoenicians in 600 BCE. In it, he mentions that the sailors described having the sun on their right as they sailed Africa's southern coast. While Herodotus found this implausible (and historians have long debated whether or not the journey happened), sailors traversing the African coast south of the Tropic of Capricorn do, indeed, have the sun to their right (north).

In the same way that the Phoenicians took the Egyptian sail and built a trading culture through its use, so the Greeks developed Phoenician letter-forms into an alphabet with which they recorded their world. From the sixth century BCE, increasing numbers of histories, geographies and coast pilots emerged. These coast pilots, or *periplus*, reported coastal journeys by way of landmarks encountered along the way. Including information on harbours, beaches, people and goods traded, they would have been useful travel guides for seafarers.

One pioneering journey, in around 320 BCE, was recorded by Greek explorer Pytheas in a manuscript called *On the Ocean*. Although the original did not survive, it is quoted in later, extant, Greek works. These have enabled historians to propose a route for Pytheas's journey, from the Greek colony of Massalia (now Marseille, France), either through the Straits of Gibraltar and then north to Brittany by sea or overland to the Gironde estuary and then north by boat; around the British Isles; and possibly further north to Iceland or Norway.

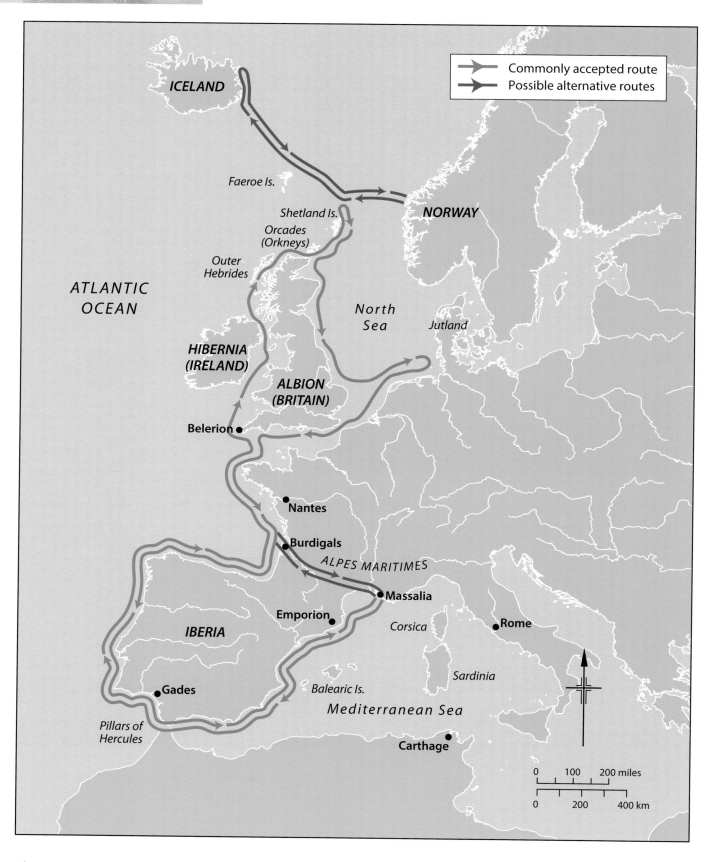

Above: *Possible routes taken by Pytheas.*

Whatever route he took, Pytheas opened Greek eyes to the Atlantic world. In particular, he enlightened them as to the sources of tin (from Cornwall) and amber (from Jutland) which were traded in the Mediterranean. His observations probably informed an account of tin-making in Britain by the Greek historian Diodorus, which conveys not only production processes but also tidal information:

Then they work the tin into pieces the size of knuckle-bones and convey it to an island that lies off Britain, called Ictis [probably St Michael's Mount in Cornwall]; for at the ebb-tide the space between this island and the mainland becomes dry and they can take the tin in large quantities over to the island on their wagons. (And a peculiar thing happens in the case of the neighbouring islands which lie between Europe and Britain, for at flood-tide the passage between them and the mainland runs full and they have the appearance of islands, but at ebb-tide the sea recedes and leaves dry a large space and at that time they look like peninsulas.)

Above: *The earliest known map, the* Imago Mundi, *depicts Earth as flat. Dated to 700–500 BCE, it comprises a circle surrounded by water, with Babylon at the centre.*

The first known map, the *Imago Mundi*, centred on Babylon and the Euphrates, and was created in around the sixth century BCE, when the world was considered to be flat. Around 300 years later, knowledge had advanced sufficiently for the Greek mathematician Eratosthenes to prove that the Earth was, in fact, a sphere and to roughly calculate its circumference. His estimate (based on the unit of the *stadium*, a measurement we cannot exactly define) was somewhere between 39,375 km (24,470 miles) and 46,250 km (28,740 miles). This is very close to the modern measurement of 40,030 km (24,875 miles).

The Greek astronomer, astrologer and geographer Ptolemy, who lived between 180 and 100 BCE, wanted to equip mapmakers with tools to represent the world as it was known to them. In his *Geography*, he suggested ways of projecting the spherical Earth on to a flat sheet, and listed 8,000 places with their geographical features and coordinates in latitude and longitude. He gleaned the information largely from accounts of voyages undertaken by seafaring merchants.

Above: *Astronomer, mathematician and geographer Ptolemy captured the world as it was known at the height of the Roman Empire.*

Any maps that Ptolemy himself may have produced were lost, but the *Geography* text survived and was rediscovered centuries later by Greek scholar Maximus Planudes in Constantinople (capital of the Eastern Roman Empire). In 1300, he reconstructed Ptolemy's maps, prompting a revival of ancient thinking on the world's geography. The first printed edition with maps (reproduced in Latin, rather than the original Greek) was published in Rome in 1477, with new editions regularly produced until 1550. This brought Ptolemy's view of the world to a wide audience.

Below: *Ptolemy's world map, seen here in a 1482 reconstruction, had a huge influence on Western cartography.*

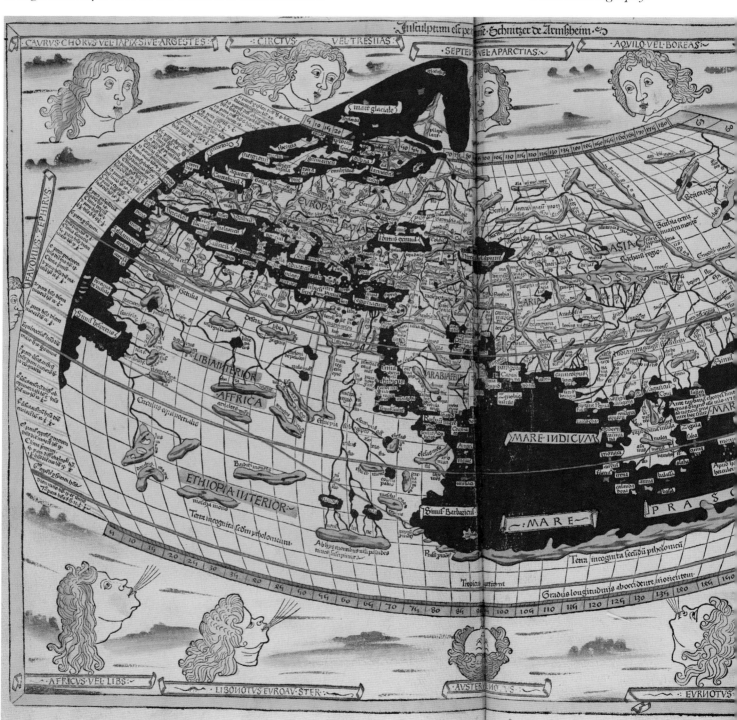

Although Ptolemy's representation of the world's geography was distorted, the topographic way he represented the world, his use of astronomical observations for locating places geographically, and how he used coordinates for reproducing locations on a map were remarkable achievements for the time. His work was far superior to the best medieval *mappaemundi* (world maps), for example. It had a huge influence on Western cartography, providing both a starting point for future maps and a model against which exploration of the world by the Europeans came to be measured.

Oldest intact shipwreck found in Black Sea

In 2018, the world's oldest intact shipwreck was discovered by scientists working in the Black Sea. Dating to around 400 BCE and believed to be Greek, the vessel is 23 m (75 ft) long and has an intact mast, rudders and rowing benches. It is most probably a trading ship, of a type known before now only from decorative pieces, such as the Siren Vase of the British Museum.

Although older vessels have been recovered from Egyptian burial sites on land, it is rare for submerged ancient ships to be so well preserved. Scientists put this lack of decay down to the unique water chemistry of the Black Sea, which is oxygen-free below 180 m (590 ft). This anoxic layer will have helped to arrest deterioration.

Lying more than 2,000 m (6,560 ft) below the surface, the wreck is among 60 submerged craft discovered as part of the three-year Black Sea Maritime Archaeology Project (MAP). This multidisciplinary Anglo-Bulgarian initiative is working to uncover the history of human activity in the area. The other discoveries range from amphorae-laden Roman trading vessels to a seventeenth-century Cossack raiding fleet.

Below: *The Siren Vase, held at the British Museum in London, depicts Greek hero Odysseus in a vessel being rowed past the Sirens (dangerous creatures believed to lure sailors on to the rocks).*

VIKING SAILORS RAID, TRADE AND SETTLE ACROSS THE ATLANTIC

Unlike the Near East and Mediterranean, much of northern Europe remained a backwater until the twelfth century. Nonetheless, northern European peoples independently developed their own maritime cultures and trading links. The Angles and Saxons honed their seafaring skills between the third and eighth centuries. We know from the Sutton Hoo burial site in Suffolk, for example, that the Saxons were capable of building sophisticated vessels and that they used bitumen from the Dead Sea region in their construction.

Rome had ruled large swathes of modern-day Europe for six centuries from 200 BCE. Between the fifth and ninth centuries, following the collapse of the Western Roman Empire in 476, a Germanic people from coastal parts of the Netherlands – the Frisians – made a name for themselves as seafarers and traders. However, it was the Scandinavian Vikings, in the ninth to eleventh centuries, who became the north European culture most renowned for its exploits on the oceans.

Left: *The Vikings navigated the seas in longships.*

Above: *Lindisfarne Priory stands on the site of an earlier monastery that was attacked by Vikings in 793.*

In 793, an attack by three ships on the Holy Island of Lindisfarne heralded the start of a series of seaborne raids by the Vikings in Britain, Ireland, France, Iberia and the western Mediterranean. The attacks, targeting monasteries, churches and towns, continued for 60 years. In subsequent years, Norse and Danish communities settled on land in Scotland, England, Wales, northwestern France, and the remote Atlantic islands of the Faroes, Iceland and Greenland.

The Vikings' farthest exploratory journey took them to North America, making them the first Europeans to arrive on the continent, almost 500 years ahead of Christopher Columbus. They first learned of the land's existence in 986, when a Norwegian sailor overshot Greenland on a voyage from Iceland and spied the eastern seaboard. Fourteen years later, Leif Erikson set out to retrace the journey. He sailed from Iceland around the west coast of Greenland, across the Davies Strait to an icy land he named Helluland (probably Baffin Island) and then south along the Labrador coast.

After stopping to explore a wooded area, he eventually arrived at a place he called Vinland (probably Newfoundland). Archaeological remains of wood-framed peat-turf buildings, discovered at L'Anse aux Meadows in 1960, confirmed that the Vikings settled in Newfoundland. Some 800 Norse artefacts were found, alongside evidence of iron production. The excavation of a more southerly site at Point Rosee in 2016 raised archeologists' hopes for further clues to Viking inhabitation of North America, but conclusive evidence from the site has so far remained elusive.

Left: *Viking Leif Erikson was the first European to reach North America.*

What is clear is that the Vikings were accomplished sailors. Voyages between Scandinavia and the British Isles, Faroe Islands, Iceland and Greenland called for open-water sailing across stretches of hundreds of miles. The Vikings were able to calculate latitude from the sun's angle and used a weighted line to determine depth. A sunstone, similar to a sundial, enabled them to account for the sun's altitude during different seasons. Aside from these rudimentary tools, however, they had to rely on their knowledge of sea states, winds, tides and the behaviour of birds and whales to get them to their destination.

Left: *The Oseberg ship was discovered by a farmer who had dug into a burial mound in Vestfold county, Norway.*

Remains in Norway and Denmark of more than 20 ships dating from the ninth and tenth centuries show that the Vikings were skilled shipbuilders, using vessels for war, trade and to convey prestige. A particularly fine example is the 26 m (85 ft) long Oseberg ship, dated to 815–820 and used in the burial of two important women. With an elegant curved prow and stern, it has the oldest indisputable evidence for a Viking sail and is also equipped with oar holes for 30 rowers. The Gokstad ship, dated to 895, is a slightly longer vessel with lower prow and stern, designed for ocean sailing.

In 2018, a Viking ship grave was detected near Oslo, using ground-penetrating radar. Ten large graves and evidence of a ship's hull were identified, placing the find among the largest ship graves ever found. Meanwhile, the first undisturbed Viking ship burial on the British mainland was excavated in Scotland the same year. Just 5 m (16 ft) long, it contained the body of a chieftain, who had been buried with his shield, sword and spear. Further investigations of these sites should yield more insights about Viking seafaring in the years to come.

Below: *The Gokstad ship would have been sailed and rowed by a crew of 34.*

The earliest divers

Humans have dived for subsistence, commerce and war for thousands of years. Pearl fishing was an early commercial form of diving. Natural pearls from *Pinctada margaritifera* and *Pinctada radiata* have been found at many archaeological sites on the Arabian Peninsula dating from 5000 to 3000 BCE, during the Neolithic period. The oldest ever found on an archaeological site, uncovered in the United Arab Emirates in 2012, was dated to 5500 BCE. At this time, pearls were gathered for aesthetic and ceremonial uses, while the shells were fashioned into fish hooks.

Left: *Alexander the Great depicted being lowered into the sea in a primitive diving bell in this image from the fourteenth-century manuscript,* The Romance of Alexander.

Natural sponges were gathered by divers in antiquity for use in cleaning, bathing and medicine. In the seventeenth century, English physicist Edmond Halley explained that these divers were 'accustomed to take down in their mouths a piece of sponge soaked in oil, by which they were able to dive for a longer period than without it'. The earliest diving bells, developed to overcome the limitations of diving on a single breath of air, date back to the fourth century BCE. Aristotle reported that Alexander the Great used one during his siege of the city of Tyre in 332 BCE.

Above: *Fishing for species such as the black-lip pearl oyster (*Pinctada margaritifera*) began thousands of years ago.*

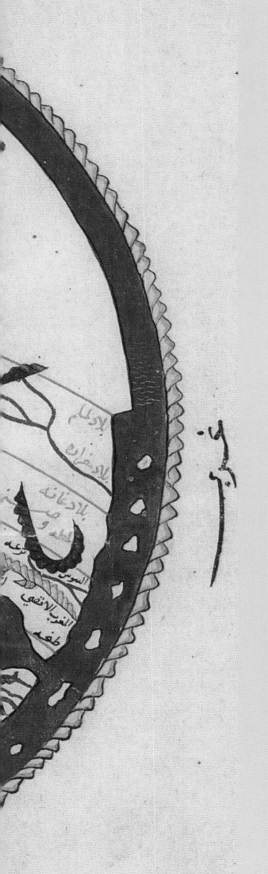

CHAPTER 2
CHINESE AND EUROPEANS MASTER LONG-DISTANCE SEAFARING

Advances in shipbuilding and knowledge of global wind patterns pave the way for major seafaring journeys by China and European nations. Exploration is driven by the desire to extend influence and control trade in valuable commodities. Maps from this time reflect the expansion of geographical knowledge through seafaring.

Left: *Al-Idrisi's world map is considered to be the best geographical work of the Middle Ages.*

ISLAMIC AND WESTERN THINKING COMBINED ON AL-IDRISI MAP

For 1,000 years, from the fall of the Western Roman Empire in 476 to the start of maritime exploration by the Portuguese and Spanish in the fifteenth century, European understanding of the Earth did not advance much beyond the ideas generated by the ancient Greeks. The risky and arduous nature of transoceanic travel still made gathering and developing knowledge about the Earth difficult. And, although many studies on the Earth's size, shape and physical features were conducted during this period, the holistic discipline of geography, as we now understand it, had yet to exist.

However, one representation of the world and its oceans stands out from this period. This is *Recreation of Journeys into Distant Lands* (also known as the *Tabula Rogeriana*), produced by the Islamic cartographer al-Idrisi. It encompassed a map of the known world engraved on a huge silver disc weighing 135 kg (298 lb), along with the volume *Recreation,* which contained supporting geographical information. Although the silver map was lost over time, ten manuscripts of *Recreation* survive. In most of these, the text is preceded by a round schematic map of the world and accompanied by 70 rectangular maps. The manuscripts reflect a period of Muslim and Western interaction.

Revealed to the Prophet Muhammad in the seventh century, the religion of Islam subsequently spread westwards across the Byzantine empire. By the early eighth century, Islamic territories were established around much of the Mediterranean Sea. As Islamic power grew, Muslims forged contacts with Christian-ruled European states, sometimes through conflict but also via diplomacy and trade. Spain became an important meeting point between Muslim and Christian worlds, as did Sicily. In the latter, for example, Islamic influences remained strong even after the Norman conquest of 1071.

Born into Moroccan royal nobility in 1099, the map-maker al-Idrisi was educated in Córdoba, Spain (a renowned Islamic centre of learning in the twelfth century) before spending a decade travelling across France, England, Asia Minor and Morocco. On reaching Palermo, Sicily, in 1138, he entered the court of the Norman king, Roger II, who put him at the heart of a project to record the 'details of his land'. King Roger II's reign was marked by tolerance between Muslims and Christians, which is reflected in how al-Idrisi combined Islamic and Western thinking in the map.

Right: *Al-Idrisi was educated in Córdoba, a renowned centre of learning in Muslim Spain.*

Al-Idrisi's work initially involved gathering the knowledge from ancient authors and the reports of contemporary travellers. As Islamic armies had stormed the Middle East and North Africa in the seventh century, they had absorbed and disseminated much Greek and Persian learning. Al-Idrisi's work was thus strongly influenced by Ptolemy's *Geography*. He emulated Ptolemy, for example, in dividing the Earth into seven latitudinal climatic zones. However, he followed the Islamic cartographic tradition of presenting the landmass of the Earth as an island, and in orienting it with south at the top.

In addition to dividing the world into the seven latitudinal belts al-Idrisi made ten longitudinal divisions, giving rise to 70 sections. Each of these was represented on one of the 70 rectangular maps presented in *Recreation*. The latitudinal climates were numbered from south to north, while the longitudinal sections were numbered from west to east. Following this pattern, al-Idrisi described each climate in turn, then detailed the important geographical and cultural features encountered by travelling east in that latitudinal belt. Cities, mountains, rivers, seas and islands were described, along with people, traded goods and regional curiosities.

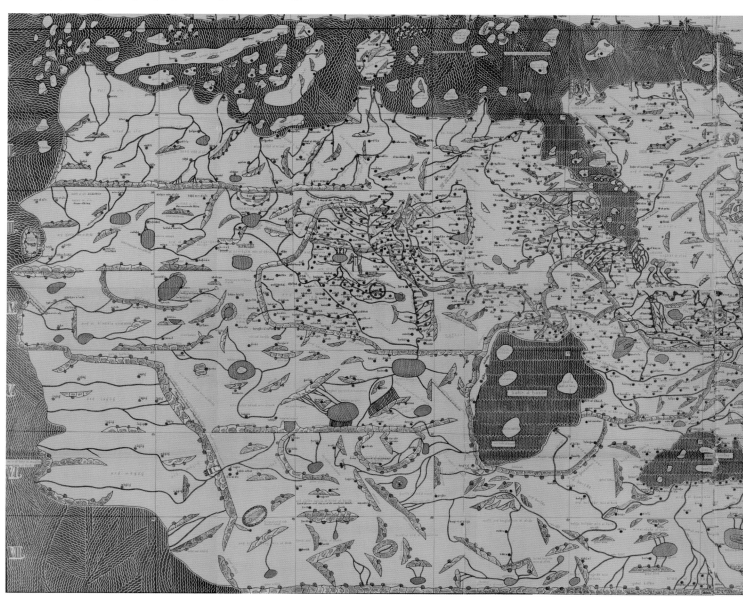

Al-Idrisi's round world map presented the Eurasian and African landmasses in their entirety, encircled by an ocean. He extended the bottom of Africa eastwards, forming a horn-shaped landmass bounding the southern Indian Ocean. Reflecting the limited knowledge of southerly latitudes, al-Idrisi's rectangular maps and text covered only the northern part of the African landmass, between the extreme north and equatorial south. Nonetheless, the work contained the greatest number of geographical places since Ptolemy's *Geography*, and gave indications of distances between them in units of miles (*mil*), three miles (*farsakh*), caravan stages (*marhala*), day marches and days of sailing.

Recreation was completed by al-Idrisi in 1154, shortly before King Roger II died. It was the first non-religious Arabic work to be printed in Europe (in Rome, in 1592), and was also reproduced in Latin, in Paris, in 1619.

Below: *Oriented with north at the bottom, as per the convention of the time, Al-Idrisi's* Tabula Rogeriana *shows Spain on the right, China on the left, Scandinavia at the bottom and Africa at the top.*

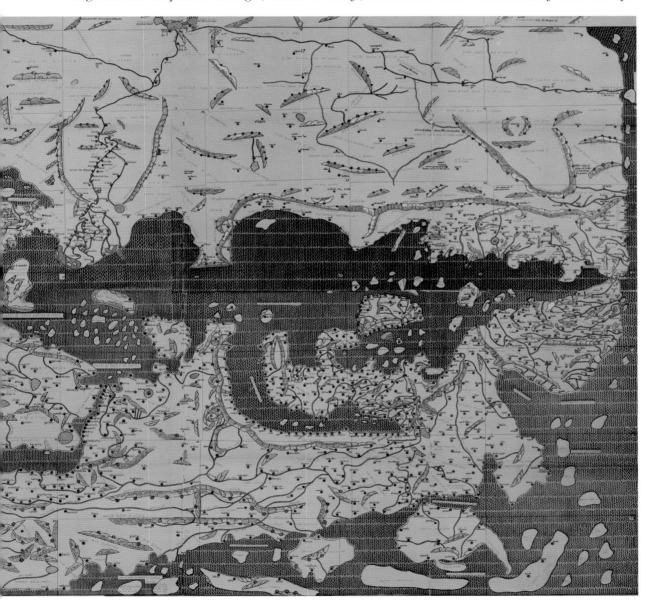

TREASURE FLEET DISPLAYS CHINA'S EARLY SEAFARING PROWESS

A lingering perception in the West is that the Spanish and Portuguese were the trailblazers of international maritime exploration in the late fifteenth and early sixteeth centuries. In fact, the Chinese were making far-reaching ocean-borne journeys a century earlier, on a scale much greater than the European voyages. Between 1405 and 1433, the Muslim eunuch Zheng He led seven maritime expeditions, each with around 27,000 participants, from China to as far afield as Africa. Some researchers believe the Chinese even sailed to the Americas before Columbus.

Prior to the start of the Ming Dynasty in 1368, China's shipbuilding skills had evolved under successive Mongol rulers. However, in the first half of the fifteenth century, the Ming Emperor Yongle elevated the nation's maritime prowess to a new level. The emperor ordered construction of an extensive fleet of oceangoing ships, including 'treasure ships' some 125 m (410 ft) long and 50 m (164 ft) wide. With nine masts apiece, these were the largest wooden ships ever built. Yongle instructed Zheng He, a military commander who had served the emperor since 1381, to command the fleet.

Right: *Zheng He, immortalized in this statue, commanded a vast fleet of ships that travelled from China as far afield as Africa.*

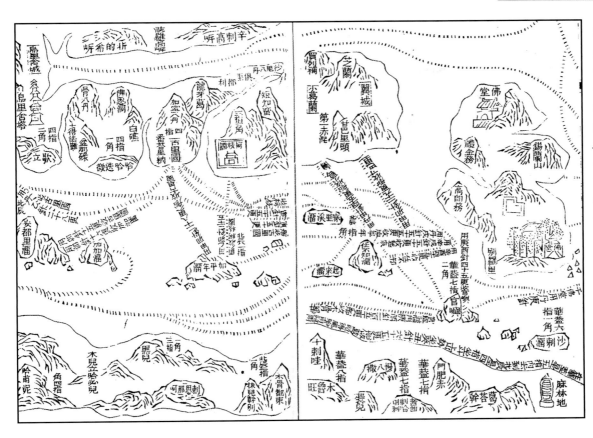

Left: *Zheng He compiled 44 sailing charts, including geographical features helpful for navigation, place names, and voyage routes.*

The first three expeditions, between 1405 and 1411, went from Nanjing to Champa (present-day southern Vietnam), up the Straits of Malacca to northern Sumatra, across the Indian Ocean to Ceylon (now Sri Lanka) and onwards to Calicut and other ports on India's southwest coast. The sailors timed each journey to coincide with the seasonal monsoon. Cold, dry northeasterly winds caused by high pressure over Central Asia facilitated their outbound travel between December and March, with moisture-laden southwesterlies from the sub-equatorial Indian Ocean bringing them home between April and August.

Above: *China's 'treasure ships' were vast in comparison to oceangoing carracks used by the Portuguese at the time.*

Following the same initial route as the preceding journeys, the fourth expedition of 1412 to 1415 also visited the Laccadive Islands, Bengal, and Hormuz in the Persian Gulf. This was the first time the Chinese had travelled beyond India. The fifth, sixth and seventh expeditions, between 1417 and 1433, went to the Arabian Peninsula and (at least in the case of the fifth and sixth) on to the east African coast. These were China's first forays on to the African continent. Apart from the final expedition, which was pared down, the fleet comprised around 250 ships, some 60 of which were treasure ships.

Right: *The Chinese used magnetic compasses and star charts to navigate.*

Right: *Emperor Yongle, seen here, instigated the early 15th-century voyages as a show of China's strength and power.*

Historians have pondered why Emperor Yongle instigated such costly and ostentatious expeditions. Whereas later Western mariners were driven to explore new lands and locate sources of sought-after commodities such as spices, it seems that the Chinese were motivated by a wish to enforce their tribute system. This system involved foreign rulers or their ambassadors visiting China to present local items as tributes to the Chinese emperor. In return for these and for acknowledging the ruler's status as the 'Son of Heaven', they received official recognition and gifts such as paper money and silk. The extensive fleet was designed to impress; however, the troops it carried were there to enforce the tribute system if local authorities did not comply.

The voyages were a clear demonstration of China's wealth, power and technical sophistication at a time when Western exploration and expansion had yet to begin. They could have marked the start of a period of Chinese colonization and commercial expansion, but they did not. Instead, increasing opposition to the extravagant expeditions led to the suspension of future voyages and the destruction of records relating to them. Ming China's presence at sea declined dramatically after 1435, as the nation became more inward-looking.

Despite the loss of records detailing the expeditions, some evidence remains. For example, Zheng He and his associates engraved inscriptions on to granite in Liujiagang (now Liuhe) on the Yangtze river and at an anchorage in Changle in Fujian as they were preparing for the final journey.

A translation of the Liujiagang inscription records the fleet's experiences: 'Whether in dense fog and drizzling rain or in wind-driven waves rising like mountains, no matter what the sudden changes in sea conditions, we spread our cloud-like sails aloft and sailed by the stars day and night.'

Meanwhile, an ancient shipyard encountered in 2015 by construction workers in Nanjing (China's capital in Zheng He's day) is believed to be the Longjiang (now Xiaguan district) site where the famed treasure ships were built. Excavations unearthed axes, hammers, nails and knives, along with a large wooden object, thought to be a rudder. The search is now on for a complete treasure ship. Several surveys have been conducted along the coast of Sri Lanka, where a treasure ship is said to have sunk as Zheng He's soldiers engaged local forces in 1410–11. Tantalizingly, the *South China Morning Post* reported in 2017 that the latest investigation had had 'positive results'. However, a significant find that will shed more light on China's medieval display of might has so far evaded the treasure-ship seekers.

Below: *A replica of the stele inscribed at Liujiagang in 1431. The text explains that Zheng He and others commanded several tens of thousands of government troops and more than 100 seagoing ships.*

DOM HENRIQUE LAYS FOUNDATIONS FOR EUROPEAN EXPANSION

The fifteenth century marked the start of overseas expansion by European nations, with Dom Henrique of Portugal (also known as Henry the Navigator) a key instigator. Born in Porto in 1394, he was the third surviving son of King Dom João I and Queen Philippa of Portugal. In 1415, Dom Henrique was involved with his elder brothers in capturing Ceuta, a Muslim port lying south of Gibraltar on the North African coast. Portugal wanted control of the port because it was through here that much gold travelling by caravan across the Sahara was funnelled. Control would also ease the passage of Christian boats through the Straits of Gibraltar.

With the establishment of Ceuta as a Portuguese enclave, Europe gained its first foothold on the African continent. Dom Henrique recognized the opportunities that this presented for further colonization; for Christianity to extend its influence over the Muslims (who inhabited northwest Africa, the Iberian Peninsula, Sicily, Sardinia, Corsica and Malta at the time); and for Portugal to intercept northbound overland trade routes even farther south, strengthening the nation's commercial position. Having further colonies in Africa would also help to justify the expense of maintaining Portugal's control over Ceuta.

Left: *Dom Henrique, depicted here, sought to expand Christianity's reach to Africa and intercept Muslim-controlled overland trading routes.*

Above: *This tilework panel by Jorge Colaço shows Dom Henrique at the battle for Ceuta.*

Rather than travel far himself, Dom Henrique motivated and supported young members of his retinue to undertake expeditions southwards along the coast of northwest Africa. Sailing past Cape Non (in southern Morocco) and beyond it round Cape Bojador (in the Western Sahara) were among the first major sailing achievements of these forays. These locations had previously held much fear for sailors because the waters around and beyond them were deemed to be highly treacherous. Once these psychological barriers had been surmounted, however, Portuguese sailors rapidly progressed farther south.

By 1442, the nation's mariners had reached Mauritania, and within a further two years they had made it to Senegal. When the Senegal and Gambia rivers were encountered soon after, Dom Henrique encouraged exploratory journeys to follow their courses inland. Two explorers that helped to open up Portuguese eyes to inland West Africa were the Genoese trader Antoniotto Usodimare and the Venetian navigator Alvide da Ca' da Mosto; the latter wrote much on the natural history and people he encountered. The realization that Africa was so vast and potentially rich in resources prompted Dom Henrique to persuade the Pope to officially recognize Portugal's right to a large stretch of the West African coast. Anyone not accepting the terms of this edict risked excommunication from the Catholic Church.

Opposite: *A sixteenth-century Portolan chart providing nautical information on Atlantic coastlines in Europe and West Africa (see box on page 71 – Portolan charts assist sailors to navigate).*

Below: *Portuguese carracks of the kind used by oceangoing merchants between the fourteenth and the sixteenth centuries.*

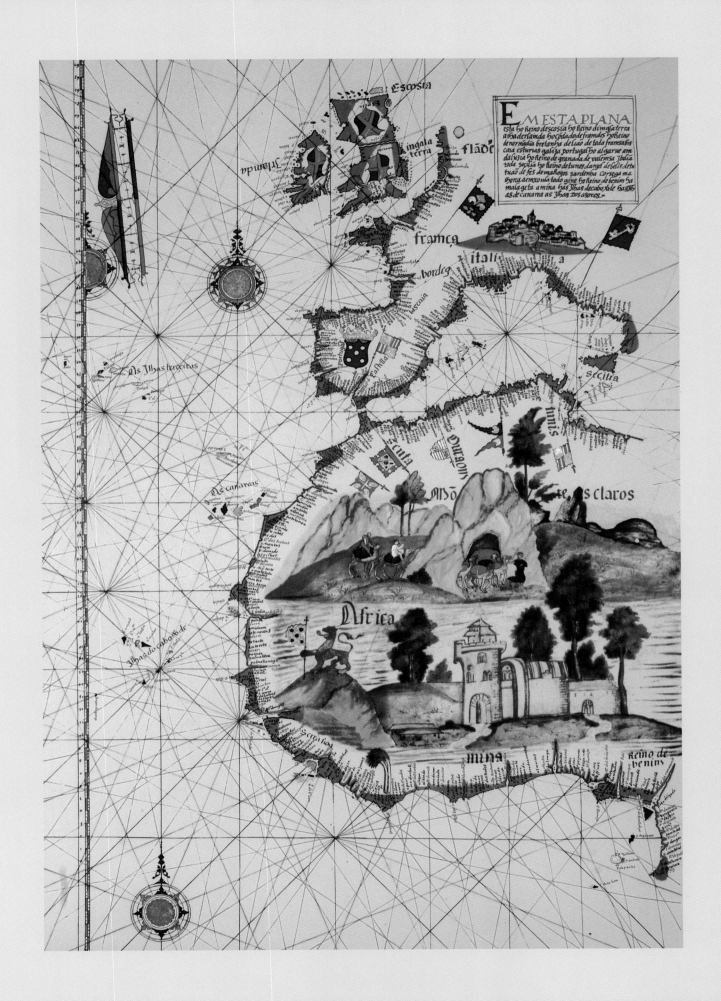

As well as eyeing West Africa for its potential for colonization and commerce, Dom Henrique was also keen to establish a Portuguese presence on islands in the Atlantic. While his attempts to overcome Spanish domination of the Canary Islands failed, the Madeira archipelago, the Azores and Cape Verde Islands were all claimed by Portugal in Dom Henrique's lifetime. An early investor in sought-after sugar cane in Madeira, he was also instrumental in the development of the trans-Atlantic slave trade. The trade began in 1444, when 235 people taken from the parts of West Africa the Europeans had reached were put up for sale in the coastal Portuguese town of Lagos. During the subsequent four centuries, Portuguese ships carried millions of Africans into slavery.

By the time Dom Henrique died in 1460, Portuguese sailors had travelled the African coast as far south as Sierra Leone. In his lifetime, he was lauded by his contemporaries for his explorative achievements in the African Atlantic. However, Renaissance scholars overinflated his place in history, crediting him with founding a School of Navigation in Sagres, Portugal, and with making major contributions to geography, astronomy, shipbuilding and scientific education. Although these claims were erroneous, he gained the name 'Henry the Navigator' as a result.

When later historians set the record straight, they somewhat downplayed Dom Henrique's role in Portuguese overseas expansion. The reality is that Dom Henrique instigated early Portuguese voyages of exploration and promoted colonization – with the support of his monarch brothers Dom Duarte (king between 1433 and 1438) and Dom Pedro (regent between 1439 and 1448) – and by doing so he added considerably to European knowledge of Earth's maritime realm. This facilitated future Portuguese expeditions that crossed the Equator, rounded the Cape of Good Hope at Africa's southern tip and navigated a sea route to Asia. It also helped to lay the foundations for one of the largest and longest-running empires in history.

Above: *Dom Henrique was involved in developing the transatlantic slave trade, which began in West Africa in 1444.*

Portuguese exploration helps advance navigation

While claims that Dom Henrique ran a school of navigation are false, the Portuguese did make navigational advances during his lifetime. By the middle of the fifteenth century, Portuguese sailors were utilizing the *volta do mar* (meaning 'turn of the sea'), a navigational manoeuvre that capitalized on the southwesterly flowing Canary current, northeast trade winds, southwest westerlies and the southeasterly flowing Portugal current to journey south down West Africa's coast and successfully return home.

The first record of any scientific observation at sea was made in 1451 by '*magistris astrologis, juxta stellas et polum viarum bene doctis*' (skilled astronomers, well versed in the stars and in the ways of the Poles) who accompanied Eleanor, a sister of King Afonso V of Portugal, on a voyage to Italy. Later, the explorer and servant to Dom Henrique, Diogo Gomes, made the first reference to an instrument being used at sea on a voyage he made in around 1460: 'I had a quadrant when I went to those parts, and I wrote the height of the arctic [sic] pole on the board of the quadrant.'

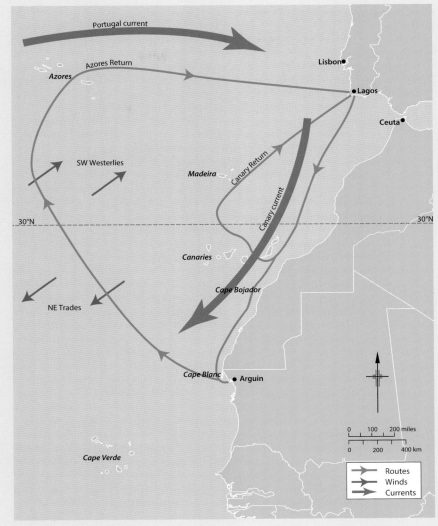

A quadrant, comprising a graduated quarter circle and sighting mechanism, is used to measure angles of up to 90°. Developed from an astrolabe (a tool employed by the ancient Greeks and early Islamic scholars to help identify celestial bodies and calculate latitudes), the quadrant was used by early sailors to measure the height of the Pole Star above the horizon, so they could work out their latitude. When northern-hemisphere sailors travelled south of the Equator, after Dom Henrique's time, they lost sight of the Pole Star below the horizon. They then measured the height of the sun above the horizon at a particular time to calculate their latitude.

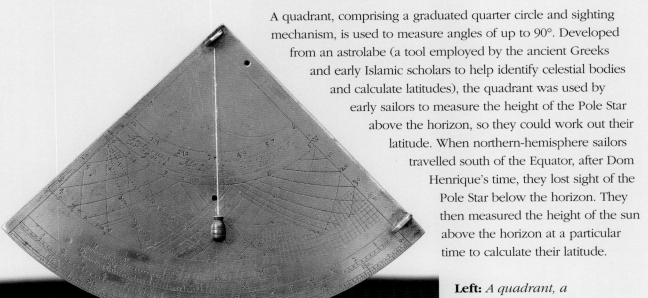

Left: *A quadrant, a navigational instrument employed by early sailors.*

SAILING WEST TO FIND SPICES REVEALS
A NEW WORLD TO EUROPE

Although Portuguese mariners had developed European knowledge of the world under Dom Henrique's direction, Western awareness of the world's global geography was still far from complete by the second half of the fifteenth century. Scholars generally accepted that the world was a sphere, but many people believed Eurasia to be a single landmass connected at its farthest reaches by the Atlantic. The extent and nature of this ocean were widely debated. Some islands, such as the Azores, were correctly located on maps, but other landmasses we now know to be non-existent were also identified.

Right: *A 1474* Mappa Mundi *by Taddeo Crivelli. At this time, most scholars thought Eurasia was a single landmass, connected at either end by the Atlantic.*

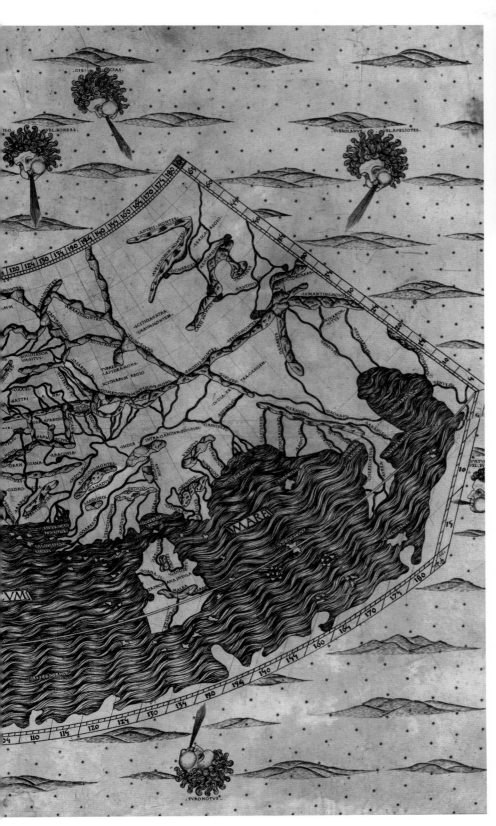

Above: *Christopher Columbus believed that sailing west would bring him to Asia.*

An attempt to find a sea route from Europe to Asia had first been made in 1291 by the Vivaldi brothers from Genoa. They had set out through the Strait of Gibraltar, seeking to reach India by circumnavigating Africa, but had disappeared en route. A motivation for such a journey was the desire to find the sources of exotic spices, which at that time were brought to Europe by Muslim traders. By the time these sought-after goods reached European shores they were very expensive; finding where they came from would enable Europeans to obtain them more cheaply and potentially break the Muslim monopoly on the trade.

It is not clear when the Genoese sea captain Cristoforo Colombo, now widely known as Christopher Columbus, decided to sail in the opposite direction to the Vivaldi brothers to try and reach Asia. However, he may have been influenced by Paolo dal Pozzo Toscanelli, a highly regarded physician and cosmographer from Florence, Italy. Toscanelli wrote in 1474 to Fernão Martins de Reriz, who had the ear of King Afonso V, about the possibility of sailing west from Europe to reach the spice regions of the East. He estimated the distance from the Canary Islands to Cipangu (Japan) to be 7,200 km (4,475 miles), and from Cipangu to Cathay (China) to be a further 3,200 km (1,988 miles). We know today that the actual distance from the Canaries to Japan is 17,000 km (10,565 miles), so he considerably underestimated the width of the Atlantic and, therefore, the potential length of the journey.

Right: *The world according to Paulo dal Pozzo Toscanelli in the mid-15th century. The physician and cosmographer's underestimate of the width of the Atlantic may have influenced Columbus's decision to sail west, rather than east around Africa, to reach Asia.*

Toscanelli and Columbus are reputed to have corresponded, though some scholars have questioned this. However, it is possible that Columbus drew on Toscanelli's representation of the world, together with other contemporary cosmological and geographical thinking, in deciding to sail west to reach Asia. He was well qualified to attempt such a voyage from a practical point of view, having sailed and traded extensively in the Atlantic between West Africa and the coast of Iceland. Moreover, advances in sail and rudder design, compass navigation, trigonometric tables, nautical charts and pilot books had improved the safety of transoceanic travel by the late fifteenth century.

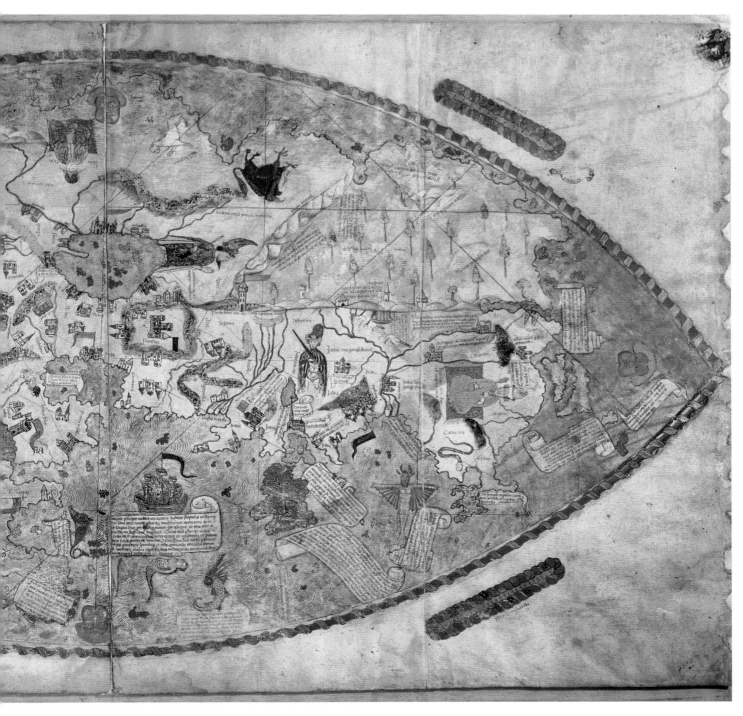

After the monarchies of Portugal, England and France turned down Columbus's request for support for an exploratory voyage west, he approached Queen Isabella and King Ferdinand of Spain. Despite a learned commission advising against the journey, believing the Atlantic to be much wider than Toscanelli's estimate, the monarchs eventually agreed to fund the expedition. In August 1492, Columbus set off from Palos de la Frontera in southwest Spain to the Canary Islands, before heading due west. He commanded three ships: the flagship *Santa María* and two smaller caravels, the *Pinta* and *Niña*. More than two months passed before one of his 96-strong crew spotted one of the islands of the Bahamas.

Columbus kept detailed diaries of his travels. Believing he had landed on an island off Japan and was now in Asia, he referred to the land he had arrived at as the Indies and to its people as Indians. One of his diary entries from October 1492 laid out his intentions:

Afterwards I shall set sail for another very large island which I believe to be Cipango, according to the indications I receive from the Indians on board. They call the Island Colba, and say there are many large ships, and sailors there. This other island they name Bosio, and inform me that it is very large; the others which lie in our course, I shall examine on the passage, and according as I find gold or spices in abundance, I shall determine what to do; at all events I am determined to proceed on to the continent, and visit the city of Guisay, where I shall deliver the letters of your Highnesses to the Great Can [an Asian emperor], *and demand an answer, with which I shall return.*

Not surprisingly, the expedition did not reach Japan or the Asian mainland; instead Columbus and his crew traversed the north coasts of Cuba and Hispaniola (an island divided today

Below: *Christopher Columbus's flagship, the* Santa Maria, *on which he explored the Caribbean, believing the islands to be part of Asia.*

Above: *A nineteenth-century depiction of Christopher Columbus's arrival in the Americas.*

between the Dominican Republic and Haiti) after their initial exploration of the Bahamas island group. In December 1492, the *Santa María* was wrecked close to Hispaniola, prompting Columbus to join the *Niña* and leave 39 crew members on the island to start a colony. He then returned home, arriving in 1493, to financial reward and the titles Admiral of the Ocean Sea and Governor of the Indies.

On hearing of Columbus's experiences, Spain was quick to seek ownership of the new territory. The Treaty of Tordesillas, agreed between Spain and Portugal from 1494, divided the world between the two nations. Lands to the west of a pole-to-pole line positioned 1,910 km (1,185 miles) west of the Cape Verde Islands were considered to be Spanish; those to the east, Portuguese. Columbus followed up his initial journey with three more trips between 1493 and 1504. On these voyages he explored the southern coast of Cuba (describing the island as a peninsula of mainland China), investigated Trinidad and Venezuela (recognizing the latter as being part of an extensive mainland) and traversed the coasts of Honduras, Nicaragua and the Isthmus of Panama.

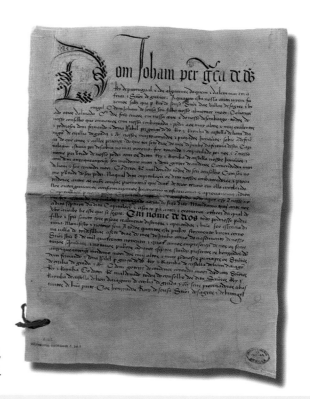

Right: *The Treaty of Tordesillas, in 1494, divided the world between Spain and Portugal.*

Columbus's early attempts to colonize the new lands he encountered failed, thwarted by hurricanes, crop failures, disease, mutinies and conflicts. However, by the time he died in 1506, more than 6,000 Spaniards had emigrated to the 'New World' and the Europeans soon overturned the native Aztec and Inca empires, gaining their wealth. Thereafter the pace of Spanish colonization accelerated, and the indigenous populations of the territories were reduced by 90 per cent due to conquest, disease and abuse.

Right: *The name 'America' likely derives from the name of Amerigo Vespucci, depicted here, who was falsely credited with being the first explorer to reach the 'New World'.*

How America got its name

In 1507, German cartographer Martin Waldseemüller published the first ever map to show the coastlines reached by Columbus and to carry the word 'America'. Waldseemüller presented his map as both a rectangular wall map and a set of 12 tapering gores top and bottom, enabling it to be stuck on to a sphere to form a globe.

Not only did the map provide a full 360° view of the world, it envisaged the north and south parts of the newly reported land as separate continents, and outlined the ocean that Magellan had yet to cross. It is not clear what made Waldseemüller place an ocean west of this land.

Why America?

A few years before the Waldseemüller map was published, Amerigo Vespucci, the banker, explorer and confidant of Columbus, had travelled to the new land. Several accounts of exploration there were subsequently attributed to him, and he was falsely credited with having 'discovered' the territory.

Waldseemüller is reputed to have used the name 'America' on his 1507 map after reading a sensationalized report of Vespucci's travels, and not realizing that Columbus, rather than Vespucci, had been the first explorer to reach the new territory. On a map produced six years later, he retracted the name but by then it had stuck and was also used to refer to North America.

A less widely accepted claim is that 'America' honoured Richard Amerike, a customs official in Bristol through whom John Cabot – explorer of the North American coastline between 1497 and 1499 – received pension payments. The suggestion is that Cabot brought the name into verbal parlance and that Waldseemüller wrongly associated it with Vespucci. However, there is little evidence to support this.

Left: *Martin Waldseemüller's 1507 map was the first to include the place name America.*

THE PIONEERING OCEAN JOURNEY THAT GAVE RISE TO AN EMPIRE

Five years after Columbus had first landed in the Bahamas, King Manuel I of Portugal dispatched seafarer Vasco da Gama to follow Bartolomeu Dias's route around Africa to try and find an easterly route to Asia (Dias having become the first sailor to round the southern tip of Africa in 1488). At this time, Spain's explorations of the so-called 'New World' were ongoing. No one had yet determined the land to be an entirely new continent and Portugal wanted to develop its own direct trading links with Asia. In particular, it wanted to locate the famed Spice Islands. These islands were believed to be the source of cloves and nutmeg brought from the East by merchants travelling the Silk Road. At the time, overland travel was long and arduous, and Muslim nations still controlled trade from the East.

Above: *Vasco da Gama, depicted here, led the first successful sea voyage from Europe to Asia in 1497–98.*

Da Gama's flagship the *São Gabriel* and three other vessels set sail from Lisbon in July 1497. The fleet first travelled with the prevailing winds southwest down the west coast of Africa to the Cape Verde Islands. Da Gama then swung out into the Atlantic, avoiding winds and currents that would have opposed his progress had he chosen to hug the coast. After sailing for three months mid-ocean, the ships then curved back east towards the Cape of Good Hope. When Africa was sighted, the ships were only one degree (112 km/70 miles) north of the Cape. From here, the vessels zigzagged up the east coast of Africa, encountering Muslim communities from Mozambique onwards.

On reaching Kenya, da Gama turned northeast across the Indian Ocean. Navigating using astronomical tables, astrolabes and quadrants, and accompanied by a pilot with knowledge

Above: *Vasco da Gama's expedition leaving Lisbon in 1497, bound for India.*

Left: *Divers investigate the wreck of the* Esmeralda, *a ship used by da Gama on a second voyage he made to India in 1502–3.*

Below: *The Port of Calicut, India, close to where Vasco da Gama landed.*

of the monsoon winds, the sailors arrived close to Calicut on India's west coast in May 1498. Having successfully found a way to bypass the Muslim countries that were controlling spices entering Europe, da Gama set about negotiating a trade deal with Calicut's ruler Samutiri Manavikraman Rajá. Despite receiving a lukewarm welcome on account of cultural differences and the leader's disdain at the Europeans' gifts, da Gama eventually received a written trading agreement. He arrived back in Portugal more than two years after his departure, having sailed 27,000 km (16,780 miles).

As reward for his success, da Gama was given titles and a pension. The trip had claimed one ship and the lives of 93 men, but da Gama had paved the way for his nation to take a controlling stake in the spice trade. Within a decade, the Portuguese had learned enough about India's ports,

monsoons, navigational characteristics and communication corridors for the nobleman Francisco de Almeida and naval commander Alfonso de Albuquerque to develop a prototype maritime empire. Fortified bases were established at strategic locations around the Indian Ocean, enabling Portugal to control key hubs on long-distance trading routes between Egypt and China. By 1512, it had reached the Moluccas, the islands that were the long-coveted source of cloves and nutmeg.

In 1998, the wreck of a ship from a second voyage to India made by da Gama between 1502 and 1503 was discovered off Oman. Excavations conducted between 2013 and 2015 yielded the ship's bell, a Portuguese coin called an *Indio* minted for trade with India, and stone cannonballs. Initials engraved on the cannonballs were interpreted as those of Vicente Sodré, da Gama's maternal uncle. This helped the archaeologists to identify the ship as the *Esmeralda*, one of five that Vicente had commanded. A further discovery of two bronze discs was confirmed in 2017 as parts of a navigational astrolabe, after scientists at the University of Warwick discerned degree markings using laser scanning technology.

The wreck is the earliest ship ever to be found and excavated from the so-called 'Age of Exploration'. While left by da Gama to patrol waters along the southwest coast of India, Vicente and his brother Bras had taken four ships, including the *Esmeralda*, on a mission to capture, loot and burn Arabian dhows in the Gulf of Aden. While sheltering at Al-Hallaniyah island, off Oman's southeast coast, two of the ships, including the *Esmeralda,* sunk in a storm. The ship's crew, along with Vicente, all died.

FIRST CIRCUMNAVIGATION DEMONSTRATES THE PACIFIC'S VAST EXTENT

When Fernão de Magalhães left Spain at the start of the first ever circumnavigation of the globe, Spain and Portugal were in dispute about European claims to the 'spice islands'. With the width of the Pacific still unknown, the general consensus was that the Moluccas lay a few days' sailing west of Mexico. Portugal claimed they were in the half of the world granted to it by the Treaty of Tordesillas; Spain felt they were in its half. The thought that any nation outside of Europe might be considered to own them did not cross the colonists' minds.

Magellan, as the English-speaking world came to know Magalhães, was a Portuguese navigator with seven years' experience in the East. He had been involved in his nation's capture of Malacca in Malaysia, and was convinced that the islands lay farther west than most people envisaged, which would place them within the Spanish half of the globe. He requested funding for an expedition from Portugal's King Manuel I; when the king was not interested, Magellan sought assistance from Spain.

With the backing of Spain's King Charles I (who would become Emperor Charles V), Magellan set sail from Sanlúcar de Barrameda in September 1519. The expedition fleet comprised five ships and some 270 men. The plan was to follow in Columbus's wake and to seek a westerly route to the East. The ships therefore travelled to the Canary Islands and southwest down the coast of Africa before crossing the Atlantic and then skirting the east coast of South America.

The expedition's main challenge was that no one in Europe knew where – or even whether – the American continent ended. The ships explored many inlets and bays as they travelled south, hoping to find a route through the landmass. Eventually they found the navigable waterway that is now known as the Straits of Magellan. The Venetian scholar and navigator Antonio Pigafetta wrote an account of the discovery, by two of the expedition ships, in *Report on the First Voyage Around the World*:

> *But on approaching the end of the bay, and thinking that they were lost, they saw a small opening which did not appear to be an opening, but a sharp turn. Like desperate men they hauled into it, and thus discovered the strait by chance. Seeing that it was not a sharp turn*

Prima ego velivolis ambivi cursibus Orbem,
Magellane novo te duce ducta freto.
Ambivi, meritoq; vocor VICTORIA: sunt mi
Vela, alæ; precium, gloria; pugna, mare.

but a strait with land, they proceeded further and found a bay. And then further on they found another strait and another bay larger than the first two. Very joyful, they immediately turned back to inform the captain-general.

By the time Magellan exited the strait in November 1520, many men had died from scurvy – having not eaten fresh food for almost four months – and only three ships remained. With minimal supplies the expedition persisted west, fortuitously carried by a favourable current, until the sailors finally spied land in March 1521. They had reached the modern-day

Above: *Of the five ships that set out on Magellan's voyage, only the* Victoria *completed the circumnavigation.*

Philippines but had lost more crew on the sail across the Pacific. Magellan also died soon after, in a skirmish with locals on the island of Mactan. With too few men left to crew the three remaining boats, the *Concepción* was scuppered in the Philippines. Juan Sebastián de Elcano and Gonzalo Gómez de Espinosa now took charge.

The *Trinidad* and *Victoria* pressed on, visiting numerous islands in their search for the Moluccas. Eventually, a Malay slave, who had been bought by Magellan in the East, taken back to Spain and then employed as an interpreter on the current journey, realized he could understand the local language and went on to recognize the Moluccan islands of Ternate and Tidore. By returning to the region from where Magellan had taken him, he may have become the first person to travel around the world.

Below: *Map from 1545 showing the route of Magellan's circumnavigation.*

From here, the *Trinidad* attempted to sail back across the Pacific to Mexico but failed and returned to the Moluccas. Here, the crew were captured by the Portuguese. The *Victoria* continued west for a further nine months to reach the Cape of Good Hope. The ship then

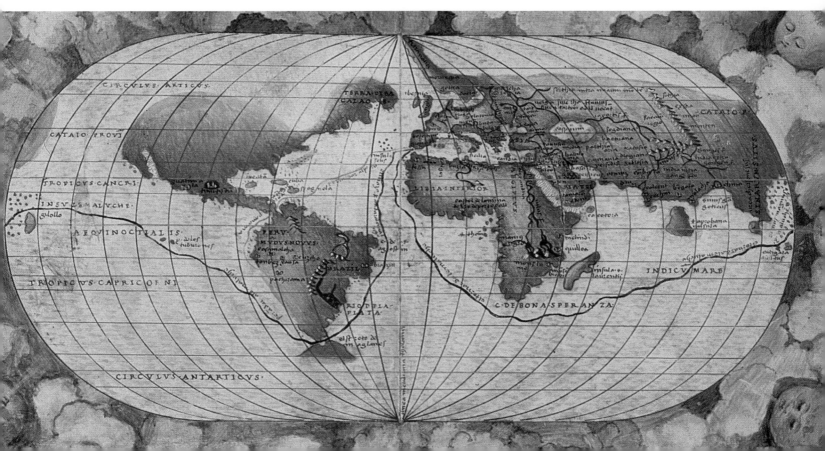

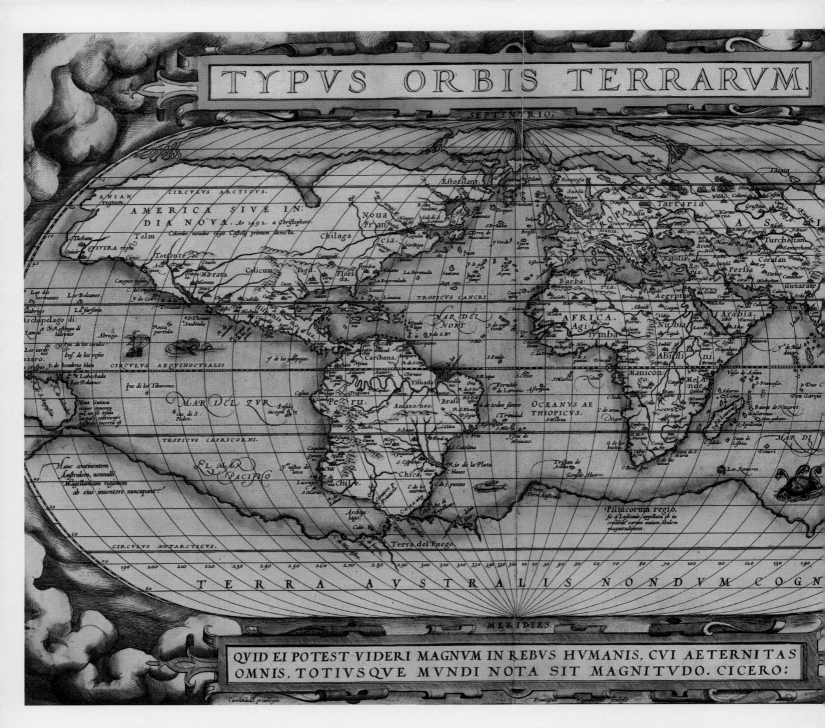

The unknown southern land

Ancient Greek geographers had wondered whether a southern landmass – Antipodes – existed. By the 17th century, this notion had become firmly established in European minds, with the fabled land becoming known as Terra Australis. Magellan did not establish that land to the south of the Straits of Magellan (Tierra del Fuego, the archipelago off the south of South America) was comprised of islands, and cosmographers of the day perpetuated the idea that the terrain was, in fact, the unknown southern continent.

Above: *Abraham Ortelius's map of 1573 shows an immense southern continent – including the words 'Nondum Cognita' (not yet known).*

sailed north along the entire west coast of Africa and across to the Cape Verde Islands before turning into the Straits of Gibraltar and arriving back at Sanlúcar de Barrameda. It was almost three years since the ship had left, and only 18 men from the original crew had survived.

Despite the immense loss of life, the expedition had succeeded in proving the Earth was spherical, charting a westerly route to the East and demonstrating that South America did not extend south to connect with the landmass of Terra Australis (see box opposite).

Invention of the compass sets the scene for safer sea journeys

The story of how the magnetic compass came into use for maritime navigation is complex. Amalfi in Italy claims to have created the first form of compass used at sea by sailors, at the turn of the thirteenth century. This was essentially a magnetic needle placed in a box with a card divided into sections and a wind rose. However, the very first compass, simply comprising a magnetic needle pointing north and south, was invented by the Chinese as far back as 1040.

It is not clear how or when the Chinese invention found its way to Europe, or, indeed, if it was independently invented there. However, we know that it was in use in the West by the second half of the twelfth century, as the English Augustinian monk Alexander Neckam mentioned it in his book *De Naturis Rerum* in 1187, observing:

> *The sailors, moreover, as they sail over the sea, when in cloudy weather they can no longer profit by the light of the sun, or when the world is wrapped up in the darkness of the shades of night, and they are ignorant to what point of the compass their ship's course is directed, they touch the magnet with a needle. This then whirls round in a circle until, when its motion ceases, its point looks direct to the north.*

Getting lost at sea had presented a great danger to early sailors, who could easily become disoriented without sight of land in bad weather. For this reason, sea journeys were limited to the summer months. Once Mediterranean sailors began using the magnetic compass in their vessels from the early fourteenth century, they were able to sail more accurately between locations, giving them the confidence to sail all year round. This contributed to a rise in trade that helped Italian city-states, such as Venice, to grow prosperous.

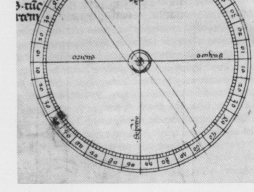

Right: *A medieval illustration of a compass.*

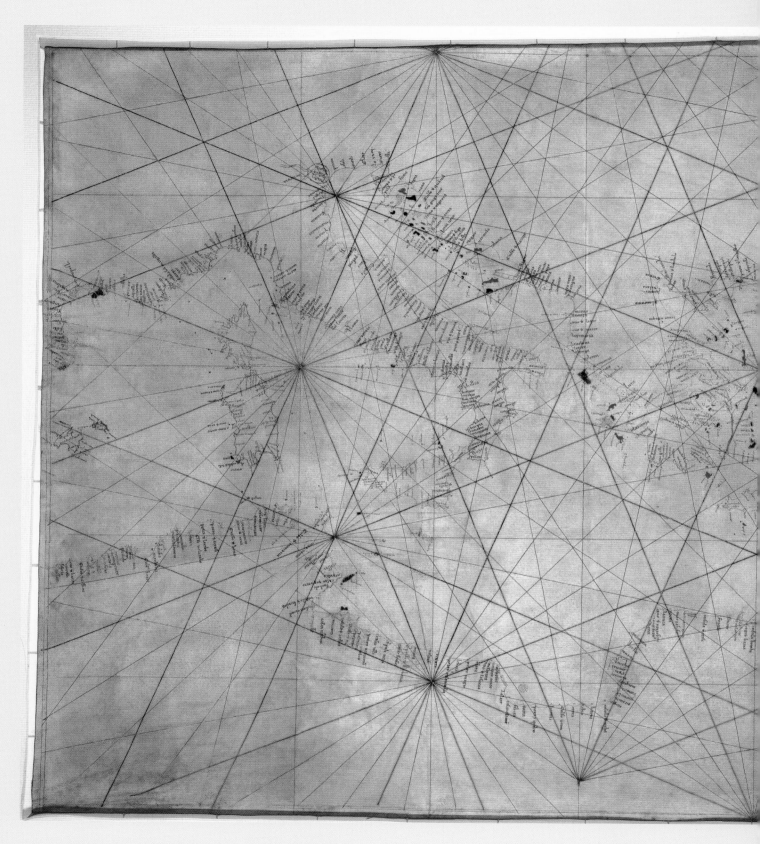

Above: *Radial networks of lines on Portolan charts helped sailors calculate the direction they must travel in between locations.*

Portolan charts assist sailors to navigate

Sometime after the invention of the compass and before the start of the fourteenth century, a new kind of sea map was developed, specifically for aiding navigation: portolan charts. The earliest surviving example dates to 1311 and these maritime aids were still in use by sailors during the eighteenth century. Some 6,000 examples survive today.

Rather than being constructed on a grid of latitude and longitude lines, they comprised a network of 16 or 32 radial lines that formed the centre of an invisible circle. This covered the bulk of the chart, with additional lines stretching from points on the circle's circumference. The lines represented magnetic compass bearings, enabling a sailor to work out the direction between two points on a chart.

The charts also depicted coastlines, with important ports labelled in red and less significant ones in black. Place names were written on the otherwise blank landmasses. Hand drawn on vellum or paper, portolan charts were initially produced in Venice, Majorca and Genoa, and covered the Mediterranean. Over time, the area of production extended to encompass multiple European locations plus a few colonies, reflecting maritime Europe's expansion – initially south and west, then beyond to the Americas, India and the Far East.

It is not clear how portolan charts were initially developed – they are very different to maps based on Ptolemy's grid system, for example – but it is likely that they were a visual representation of years of accumulated knowledge on how to sail from one place to another. At the time they came into use, sailors had to rely on dead reckoning to determine their position at sea. This required four pieces of information: the known or assumed starting position; the vessel's bearing; its speed; and the time spent travelling on each bearing at each speed.

Sailors could estimate latitude using the measured angle of Polaris above the horizon or the height of the sun at local noon. They estimated their ship's speed by marking two points on its side, casting a piece of wood into the sea and using their pulse or a number of paces to estimate the time taken by the wood to pass between the two marks. A Mediterranean navigator equipped with a portolan chart, set of dividers and a compass would have been able to plot a position on the chart, work out the bearing needed to travel to a given destination, and derive rough estimates of their vessel's position along the way.

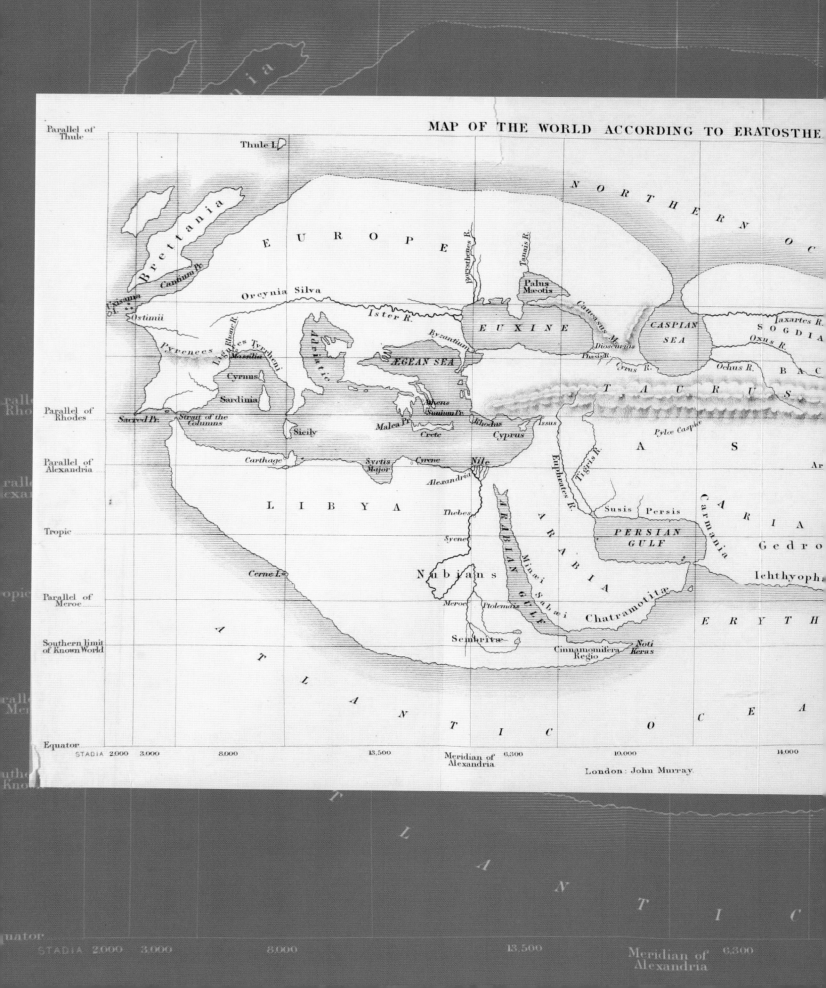

MAP OF THE WORLD ACCORDING TO ERATOSTHE[NES]

London: John Murray.

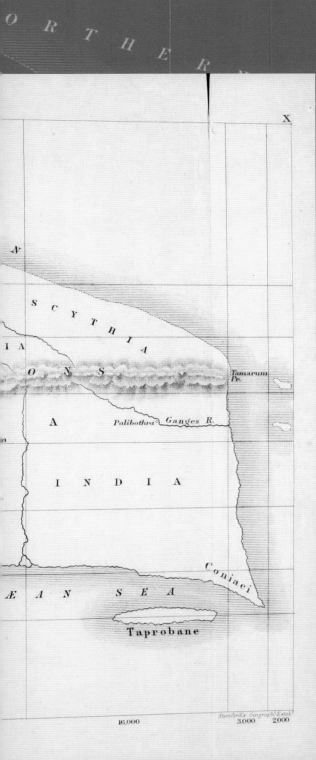

CHAPTER 3
SAILORS BENEFIT FROM NAVIGATIONAL AND MAP-MAKING PROGRESS

Ocean voyages are made easier by navigational and cartographic advances, including the ability to calculate longitude. Europeans gain a better understanding of world geography, following Cook's circumnavigation. And knowledge grows of the Atlantic's currents and winds, after North America's colonization.

Left: *Greek geographer Eratosthenes pioneered using latitude and longitude to divide the world horizontally, as seen here on his map from around 220 BCE.*

LACK OF LONGITUDE LIMITS MARITIME PROGRESS

The increasing number and ambition of sea journeys from the fifteenth century called for a reliable means of calculating a vessel's position when out of sight of land. The system that offered the best means to achieve this was latitude and longitude. Devised by the Greek mathematician, geographer and astronomer Eratosthenes some 220 years BCE – and still valid today – this method divides the globe horizontally into slices and vertically into segments, with latitude being the distance north or south of the Equator, and longitude the east-west distance.

The position of lines of latitude, or parallels, is measured in degrees north or south away from the Equator (0°). The position of lines of longitude, or meridians, is today measured from 0° to 180° east or west from Greenwich, UK. This location has been internationally recognized as the prime meridian (0°) since 1884. So today we give the coordinates of Madrid, Spain, as approximately 40°N, 4°W; Mumbai, India, as 19°N, 73°E; and Buenos Aires, Argentina, as 35°S, 58°W, for example. Before 1884, sailors measured longitude from their port of origin.

As we learned in Chapter 2 (see page 55), mariners could calculate latitude by the fifteenth century. In the northern hemisphere they did so using the Pole Star, which lay close to the northern celestial pole. This meant that sailors could use the reducing height of the Pole Star as they approached the Equator as a proxy for latitude. They simply aligned the sights on a quadrant with the star, then observed where the instrument's plumb line crossed the scale. This gave a figure for the angle between the Pole Star and the parallel at which the vessel lay. Adjustments to account for the star's rotation of a few degrees about the pole yielded a figure for latitude.

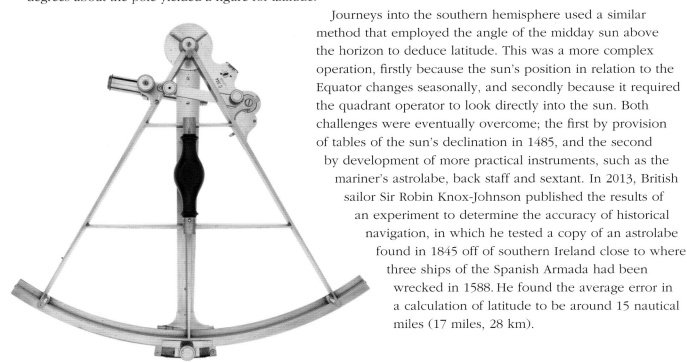

Above: *How parallels of latitude and meridians of longitude are calculated on the globe.*

Journeys into the southern hemisphere used a similar method that employed the angle of the midday sun above the horizon to deduce latitude. This was a more complex operation, firstly because the sun's position in relation to the Equator changes seasonally, and secondly because it required the quadrant operator to look directly into the sun. Both challenges were eventually overcome; the first by provision of tables of the sun's declination in 1485, and the second by development of more practical instruments, such as the mariner's astrolabe, back staff and sextant. In 2013, British sailor Sir Robin Knox-Johnson published the results of an experiment to determine the accuracy of historical navigation, in which he tested a copy of an astrolabe found in 1845 off of southern Ireland close to where three ships of the Spanish Armada had been wrecked in 1588. He found the average error in a calculation of latitude to be around 15 nautical miles (17 miles, 28 km).

Knox-Johnson reasoned that a lookout positioned 21 m (70 ft) up on the masthead of a late-fifteenth-century vessel could expect to see a familiar 61 m (200 ft) hill from 42 km (26 miles) away. He therefore concluded that 15 nautical miles was an acceptable level of error, which enabled sailors to reach their destination relatively easily. Knowing the latitude of their destination,

Opposite: *A sextant, used by sailors to estimate latitude by calculating the altitude of the sun or stars above the horizon.*

Above: *In the 15th and 16th centuries, mariners such as explorer Amerigo Vespucci, depicted here, calculated their latitude using the stars.*

they steered the ship to that parallel and then remained on it to the end point. The invention of Mercator's map projection in 1569 simplified this process (see box on pages 78–79 – Mercator's view of the world aids navigation at sea).

While being able to calculate latitude relatively accurately was undoubtedly helpful to the development of maritime exploration, the pressure to find a way of calculating longitude – thereby pinpointing a ship's exact location – became increasingly great in the seventeenth century. By now, merchant and naval shipping was

expanding, as new nations sought a share of burgeoning international trade. Spain and Portugal no longer held sway; the Dutch Republic, England and France, as well as lesser parties such as Denmark, Sweden, Austria, Prussia and English colonies in North America and the West Indies, were now also vying for control of trade routes and foreign territories.

Below: *A scene depicting the Anglo-Dutch war of 1666, fought over the control of trade routes.*

The limitations of early navigation meant ships had to follow favourable winds and often could not take the most direct routes between places. This forced the rival nations to follow the same oceanic courses, bringing them into frequent contact. Seaborne battles often broke out, as each sought to capture its rivals' goods and territories while defending its own vessels and lands. It also made journeys very long; a round trip between Europe and the East could take two years. Not only did this make communication difficult between commercial agents in Europe and those in the field, it also made recruiting seamen a challenge. The longer mariners spent at sea, the higher their risk of dying from scurvy through a lack of vitamin C. (The cause of scurvy was not understood at this time.)

Not being able to calculate longitude forced navigators to be conservative in their choice of sea routes. Travelling on a direct bearing to the destination risked under- or overshooting it and then

Mercator's view of the world aids navigation at sea

Mapping a three-dimensional globe on to a two-dimensional sheet inevitably produces distortions. In the latter half of the sixteenth century, cartographers tended to use elliptical projections to produce maps. These portrayed each degree of latitude or longitude faithfully (while latitude parallels never grow closer to each other, longitudinal meridians are widest apart at the Equator and converge at the poles). However, they were difficult for sailors to navigate by, as lines depicting a 'straight' compass bearing appeared curved. This meant that ships had constantly to recalculate their bearing as they sailed.

In 1569, Flemish cartographer Gerardus Mercator produced a new kind of wall map with a cylindrical projection. Although this distorted features lying close to the poles, it preserved 90° angles between lines of longitude and latitude. Sailors' bearings also appeared straight, rather than curved, making them much easier to follow. You can get a rough idea of how this projection worked by imagining a glowing globe inside a tube, picturing where the shadows of longitude and latitude fall on the inside of the tube, and then uncurling the cylinder to form a flat two-dimensional sheet.

Eventually, Mercator's projection began to be used in navigational charts, and enabled navigators to more easily work out the bearing they should follow to reach a desired destination. In recent years, Mercator's projection has been criticized for the way it distorts landmasses with distance from the Equator (for example, Greenland appears to be the same size as Africa when, in fact, it is much smaller). However, it is still used in some nautical, aerial and military maps, and many online map providers use a variation called Web Mercator.

Above: *Elliptical projections portray latitude and longitude faithfully but make straight compass bearings between two points appear curved.*

GERARDI MERCATORIS RVPELMVNDANI EFFIGIEM ANNOR·
DVORVM ET SEX — AGINTA,SVI ERGA IPSVM STVDII
CAVSA DEPINGI CVRABAT FRANC. HOG. CIƆ. IƆ. LXXIV.

Left: *Cartographer Gerardus Mercator.*

not knowing if the vessel was too far east or west of the location in question. Sailors therefore headed for a point that was a fair distance east or west of where they wanted to go. That way, once they reached the correct latitude, they could simply travel along that parallel until they arrived at their port of call. Overcoming this challenge had the potential to make navigation less error-prone, and to therefore reduce the number of lives, goods and vessels lost at sea (see box on page 80 – A great maritime disaster). As early as 1598, Spain offered a substantial financial incentive to the 'discoverer of the longitude'. The Dutch Republic put forward a similar reward a few decades later and other nations offered similar incentives. Only after 1714, however, when the British government offered by Act of Parliament a Longitude prize of £20,000 to whoever could calculate longitude to within half a degree (around two minutes of time) was an accurate method for calculating longitude devised.

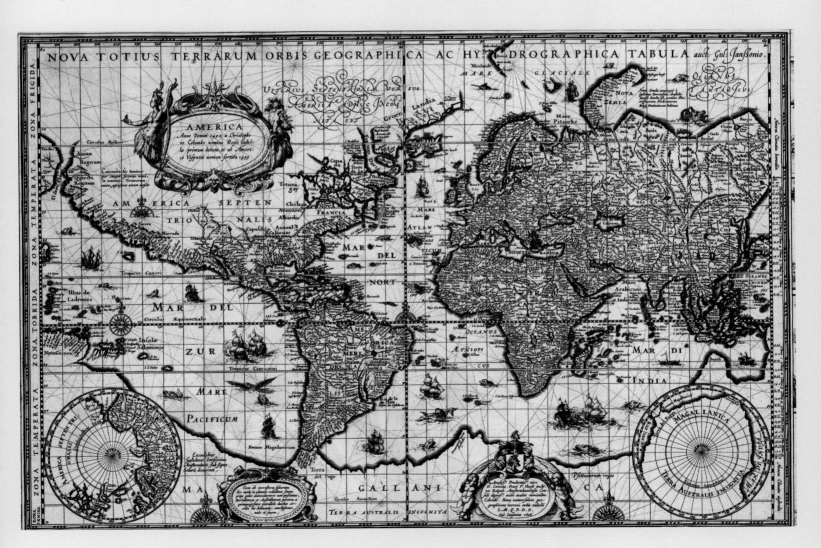

Above: *Mercator's new projection maintained 90°
angles between lines of longitude and latitude.*

A great maritime disaster

The sinking of HMS *Association* in 1707 off of the Scilly Isles added impetus to calls to improve navigational knowledge. This 96-gun, 1,459-ton vessel was the flagship of Sir Cloudesley Shovell during the war of the Spanish Succession (triggered by the death of the childless Charles II of Spain). When the vessel and three others sank while returning from the Mediterranean, Shovell and 2,000 of his men were lost. Forty-four surviving log books record errors in longitude – calculated using dead reckoning – of between one and three degrees.

Commander-in-Chief of the British Fleets, Shovell had, himself, expressed an interest in how navigation might be improved; he had met astronomer Isaac Newton in 1699 to discuss one proposal put forward for calculating longitude. The loss of such a high-ranking individual and so many men was considered the worst maritime disaster of the age. It was later cited in lobbying for a bill to reward whoever 'found' longitude.

When the wreck was investigated in 1967, archaeologists found 'pieces of eight' – the world's first global currency – famed for being used by pirates.

Above: *The loss of 2,000 lives off of the Scilly Isles in 1707 was deemed the worst maritime disaster of the age.*

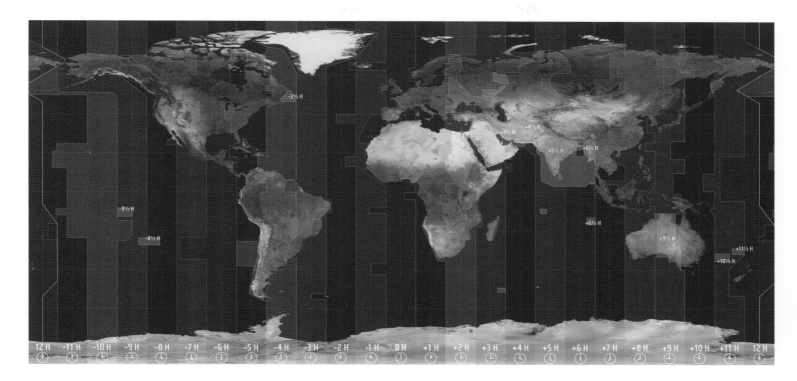

Above: *This standard time-zone map shows how times around the world relate to longitude.*

PRIZE PROMPTS INNOVATION THAT CRACKS LONGITUDE PUZZLE

The science behind calculating longitude is relatively simple. The Earth turns 15° of longitude each hour, completing a full 360° rotation in 24 hours. The line of longitude experiencing solar noon – that is, the time at which the sun is at its highest point in the sky that day – changes as the Earth turns. Noon at, say, Longitude A, occurs one hour earlier than noon 15° to the west of that longitude. If you sail west from Longitude A, therefore, you will have travelled 15° of longitude when noon on your ship takes place one hour after noon at Latitude A.

As far back as the early sixteenth century, academics had understood that this method could be used to calculate longitude. What evaded them, however, was the means of knowing the time at a location other than the one they were in. Being able to carry a machine set at the time of the remote location was a possible solution. The first timepiece capable of accurately keeping time, the pendulum clock, was invented in 1657. However, the motion of the sea ruled it out as a potential means for sailors to carry time with them on voyages.

Scientists instead focused on the possibility of using an astronomical clock. The hope was that sailors might be able to use the position of stars or other celestial bodies to help them identify the time at a distant location. The Royal Observatory was founded in Greenwich in 1675, seeking the 'rectifying of the tables of the motions of the heavens and the places of the fixed stars, in order to find out the so much desired longitude at sea, for perfecting the art of navigation'. In 1725 it published a catalogue giving data on 3,000 observable stars.

Below: *The Royal Observatory in Greenwich, UK, was founded in 1675 with the aim of using astronomy to calculate longitude.*

By the middle of the eighteenth century, a lunar method of calculating longitude was gaining favour. This sought to take advantage of the moon's relatively quick passage, past several known stars, across the sky. Tables were needed giving the time in Greenwich when the moon and a particular star were separated by a certain angle. Sailors on board a ship could calculate the time where they were when a particular angle between the moon and star was observed, use such tables to work out the time in Greenwich, and then use the difference between 'Greenwich time' and their time to calculate longitude.

Tables produced by German professor Tobias Mayer were found by the Royal Observatory to be accurate to within one degree. This was a much greater level of accuracy than could be achieved by dead reckoning. A successful test of the method by Dr Nevil Maskelyne on a voyage to St Helena led to publication of a guide to using the lunar method to calculate longitude and, from 1767, annually published data on the lunar distances of the sun and seven stars at three-hourly periods. Despite this apparent solution to the longitude problem, the method was highly impractical. Early practitioners noted that it could take four hours and four people to calculate a single position.

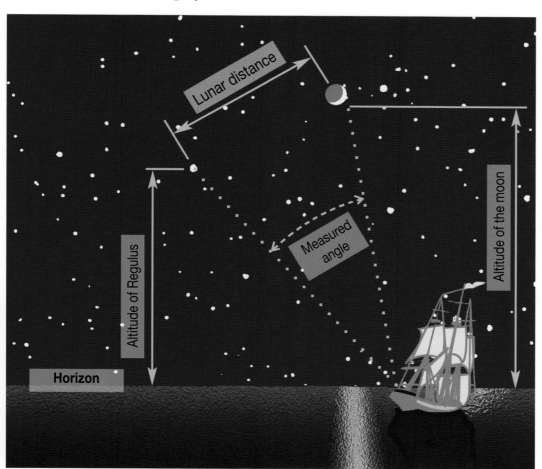

Above: *Dr Nevil Maskelyne, who successfully tested a lunar method for calculating longitude in 1767.*

Left: *Illustration of the lunar distance method of calculating longitude. 'Lunar distance' refers to the angle between the moon and another celestial body, in this case the star Regulus, the brightest star in the constellation of Leo.*

While the lunar method was being developed, British carpenter John Harrison was applying himself to making a pendulum-less clock which would be able to withstand the rigours of life at sea. He devised a new form of timekeeper, made from brass, steel and wood, which had dumbbell-shaped bar balances instead of a pendulum. Sea tests of the clock – H1, weighing 34 kg (77 lb) – proved promising and the Board of Longitude, administrators of the Longitude Prize, gave Harrison £250 to continue with his work. They promised, in 1737, to provide a further £250 on approval of an improved version of the clock.

Over the next three decades, with further financial support from the Board, Harrison completed two further versions of his innovative timekeeper before deciding to adopt, and try to improve, existing watch technology. This gave rise to the marine timekeeper H4, essentially a large watch that ticked five times per second, in a silver case. When H4 was tested on a journey from Portsmouth to the West Indies in 1761, the operator was able to accurately predict the ship's arrival time in both Madeira and Jamaica.

Although H4 appeared to have met the conditions of the Board of Longitude's £20,000 prize of determining longitude to within half of a degree, the Board was not so easily won over. It said it could not confirm the timekeeper's success because the longitude of Port Royal in Jamaica was not properly known and the watch's 'rate' – the amount of time lost or gained each day – had not been agreed prior to the test. The Board admitted that H4 was 'an invention of considerable utility to the public', but refused to authorize payment of the prize.

Instead, Harrison was offered £2,500, with £1,500 to be paid immediately and the remainder on conclusion of a second trial. Over the 46 days of this next voyage, to Barbados in 1764, the timekeeper again performed with great accuracy. The official error was 39.2 seconds of time, or less than ten nautical miles in the latitude of Barbados.

Harrison felt that this success should have gained him the full prize money. However, the Board wanted to know that Harrison's method could be replicated so that it would ultimately benefit the public. The Board therefore recommended that Parliament award Harrison £10,000

Above: *John Harrison, who strived to make an accurate timepiece that sailors could carry at sea.*

H1

H2

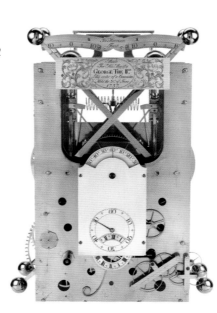

Left and Opposite: *John Harrison's first four timepieces.*

A new Longitude Prize for a modern dilemma

Three hundred years after the Longitude Prize was first launched, the British government convened a new Longitude Committee in 2013 to identify the six biggest global issues facing the world. Led by today's Astronomer Royal Lord Martin Rees, the group of more than 40 leading scientists, engineers and politicians examined themes of energy, environment, global development, technology and robotics, democratizing access to communications, and health and wellbeing. They identified six potential challenges, which were then put to a public vote.

The public voted for the challenge: How can we prevent the rise of resistance to antibiotics? The new Longitude Prize fund of £10 million (approximately equivalent to the top £20,000 prize offered in 1714) will pay out £8 million to the person or team that develops an accurate, rapid, affordable and globally usable diagnostic test capable of revolutionizing healthcare and leading to the conservation of antibiotics for posterity. Entries are assessed every four months, with the anticipation that the prize will be won between 2015 and 2020. The Longitude Prize is run by a team from Nesta, the UK's innovation foundation.

when he demonstrated how the watch worked and a further £10,000 (minus monies already paid) once it was proven that other makers could produce timekeepers of similar quality and accuracy.

These conditional recommendations – together with proposals to award £3,000 to Mayer's heirs; £300 to Leonhard Euler for work to develop accurate lunar tables; and £5,000 to anyone who could improve Mayer's tables in future – became law in a new Longitude Act of 1765. Despite Harrison's grievances with the Board, he continued to hone his invention, producing H5 in 1772. When King George III tested H5 at his observatory in Richmond, he found it to be highly accurate and advised Harrison to petition Parliament for justice over the unpaid prize money.

Through this process Harrison was awarded £8,750 by Parliament, which was more than the difference between monies paid to him by the Board during the development of his timekeepers and the £20,000 prize money. However, he was 80 when he received the money, and died three years later. The actual Board of Longitude Prize was never awarded. The question as to whether it should have been awarded to Harrison after the Barbados trial largely comes down to interpretation: was the prize for a single timekeeper that could accurately calculate longitude or was it for the means to 'mass-produce' one, which could only be proved by replicating the model. This point is still debated today.

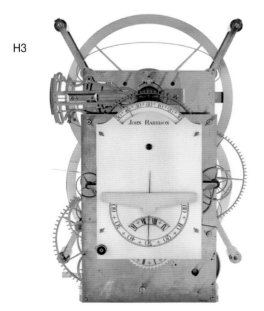

H3

H4

On the 300th anniversary of the original prize, a new competition was launched, seeking to resolve a modern-day global challenge through innovation (see box above – A new Longitude Prize for a modern dilemma).

COOK ENLIGHTENS EUROPE AS TO SOUTHERN HEMISPHERE GEOGRAPHY

In 1767 the British cartographer Alexander Dalrymple had argued that the fabled 'unknown southern land' did exist, after compiling possible sightings by navigators in *An Historical Collection of the Several Voyages and Discoveries in the South Pacific Ocean*. The following year, an expedition funded jointly by the Royal Society and the Admiralty despatched Captain James Cook to the Pacific island of Tahiti (which had been brought to British attention the previous year by explorer Samuel Wallis). The Royal Society wanted Cook to observe the passing of Venus between the Earth and sun with a view to gathering measurements that could help calculate Earth's distance from the sun. Cook's secret mission from the Admiralty, however, was to search for lands in the South Pacific, including the 'southern continent'. The expedition, and those that followed, provided an opportunity to test the new methods for calculating longitude.

Above:
James Cook, leader of the Endeavour *expedition of 1768–1771.*

Cook had gained knowledge of navigation, mathematics and astronomical observation working in the North Sea coal trade before joining the Royal Navy in 1755 and serving in North America. These experiences, which included time spent observing an eclipse of the sun and charting the St Lawrence River and various coastal areas, made him an ideal candidate for leading the expedition. So it was that Cook sailed on HMS *Endeavour* from Plymouth in August 1768, arriving in Tahiti in April 1769. After establishing relations with the Tahitians and successfully observing the transit of Venus, Cook sailed south as far as 40° in search of new lands. At this latitude in conditions of 'very strong gales, and heavy squalls of rain … and having not the least visible signs of land', Cook turned west, as instructed, and headed for New Zealand.

On discovering new land or islands, Cook had instructions to explore:

> *…as great an extent of it as you can, carefully observing the true situation thereof both in latitude and longitude, the variation of the needle, bearings of headlands, height, direction and course of the tides and currents, depths and soundings of the sea, shoals, rocks etc., and also surveying and making charts and taking views of such bays, harbours and different parts of the coast, and making such notations thereon as may be useful either to navigation or commerce.*

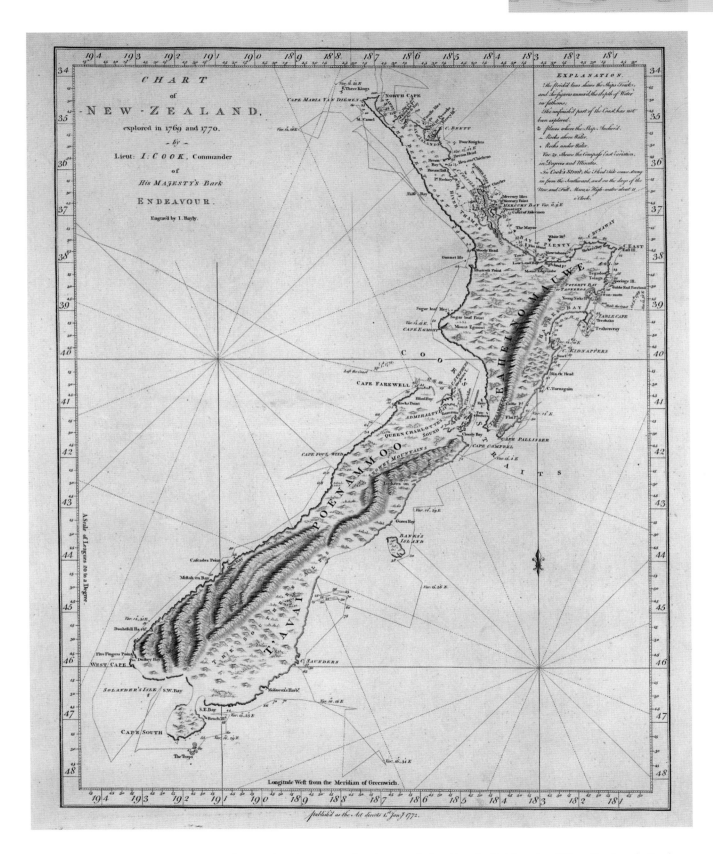

Above: *By circumnavigating and charting both islands of New Zealand, Cook proved the country was not part of a larger continent.*

Above: *HMS* Endeavour*, the ship on which Cook was sent to seek the fabled 'southern continent'.*

On reaching New Zealand (which had previously been only briefly visited from Europe by Dutchman Abel Tasman in 1642), Cook spent six months charting 3,860 km (2,400 miles) of coastline, demonstrating by circumnavigating both islands that New Zealand was not part of a larger continent. From here the expedition moved on to Australia, where Cook and his men surveyed 3,220 km (2,000 miles) of the east coast.

From Australia, the *Endeavour* continued north and west to Batavia (now Jakarta in Indonesia), their route via the Torres Strait proving that New Holland (as Australia was then known) and New Guinea were not connected. From Indonesia, the expedition sailed around the Cape of Good Hope and north to England, arriving in July 1771. In addition to fulfilling its astronomical aims, the

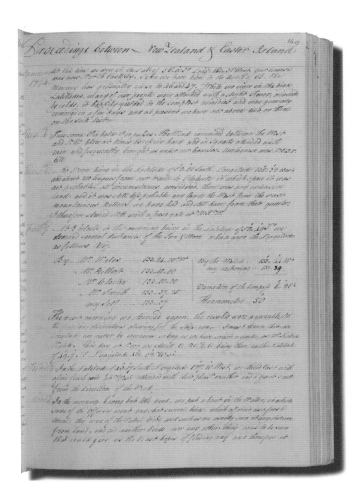

expedition provided valuable detail on lands previously unknown to Europeans and enabled Cook to claim the east coast of Australia for Britain, paving the way for colonization there. It had also delivered vast collections of floral and animal specimens, together with illustrations, thanks to the presence on board of philanthropist and botanist Joseph Banks, and several naturalists and artists funded by him on the journey. The one thing the expedition had not done, however, was to locate the fabled southern land. In a letter Cook sent to the Admiralty from Batavia, Cook concluded that 'the discoveries made this voyage are not great' as he had 'failed to discover the so much talk'd of southern continent (which perhaps do not exist)'.

Left: *Cook kept a detailed journal of his travels.*

Below Left: *Cook used the name Botany Bay to describe the point where he first landed in Australia, on account of the diverse flora found there.*

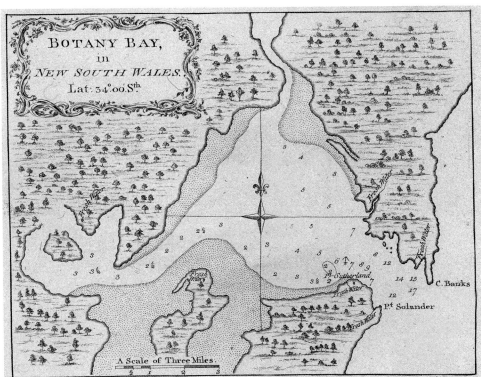

The lack of such a discovery provided the impetus for a second expedition. A year after his return, Cook departed England once more on HMS *Resolution*, accompanied by Tobias Furneaux in HMS *Adventure*. After reaching the Cape of Good Hope, the ships sailed from Africa towards Antarctica, hoping to encounter land sighted by the French in 1738. When they failed to do so, Cook followed instructions that directed him to search for land: 'Either to the Eastward or Westward as your situation may then render most eligible, keeping in as high a Latitude as you can, & prosecuting your discoveries as near to the South Pole as possible; And you are to employ yourself in this manner so long as the condition of the Sloops, the health of their Crews, & the State of their Provisions will admit of it …'

Left: *HMS* Resolution *and HMS* Adventure *moored up at Maitavie Bay on the island of Tahiti during Cook's second voyage.*

In January 1773, the ships became the first known to have crossed the Antarctic Circle at latitude 66.5°. They proceeded south until, at 67° 15' south, Cook observed: 'The ice was so thick and close that we could proceed no further.' He therefore sailed to New Zealand, from where he made a trip to Tahiti and nearby islands, stopping off on the return voyage at islands Abel Tasman had visited and which Cook named the Friendly Islands. When the *Resolution* and *Adventure* became separated in a storm, the *Adventure* returned to Britain, but Cook headed south again, crossing the Antarctic Circle twice more in December 1773 and January 1774 and eventually encountering the ice sheet that Cook wrote 'extended East and West in a streight [sic] line far beyond our sight'. The search for the great southern continent had revealed only iceberg-ridden seas and an uninhabitable ice sheet.

Cook headed back to the Pacific and set about locating Easter Island, which he landed on in March 1774. From there he revisited Tahiti and Tonga, charted islands that were at that point unknown to the British (Vanuatu, New Caledonia and Norfolk Island) and traversed parts of the Pacific that he had not explored the previous summer. When back at the southern tip of South America, Cook wrote: 'I have now done with the SOUTHERN PACIFIC OCEAN, and flatter my self that no one will think that I have left it unexplor'd, or that more could have been done in one voyage towards obtaining that end than has been done in this.' In the Atlantic, Cook encountered lands we now know as South Georgia and the South Sandwich Islands. He returned to England in July 1775, a little more than three years after he had set off. After 110,000 km (68,000 miles) of sailing, he had laid the myth of *Terra Australis* to rest and located Pacific islands that had previously been unknown to Britain.

Cook began a third voyage in July 1776, to search for the Northwest Passage, a desired navigable way connecting the North Pacific and North Atlantic Oceans, potentially providing a shorter trade route to Asia. In 1778 he encountered the Hawaiian Islands for the first time before sailing north to the Bering Sea and into the Arctic Ocean. No navigable passage was found, but the expedition did sight the eastern coast of Asia. Cook returned to Hawaii at the end of the year to spend winter there but was killed early in 1799 when a violent argument broke out between some of the sailors and locals. The expedition continued on without him, eventually abandoning the search for the Northwest Passage and returning to England in 1780.

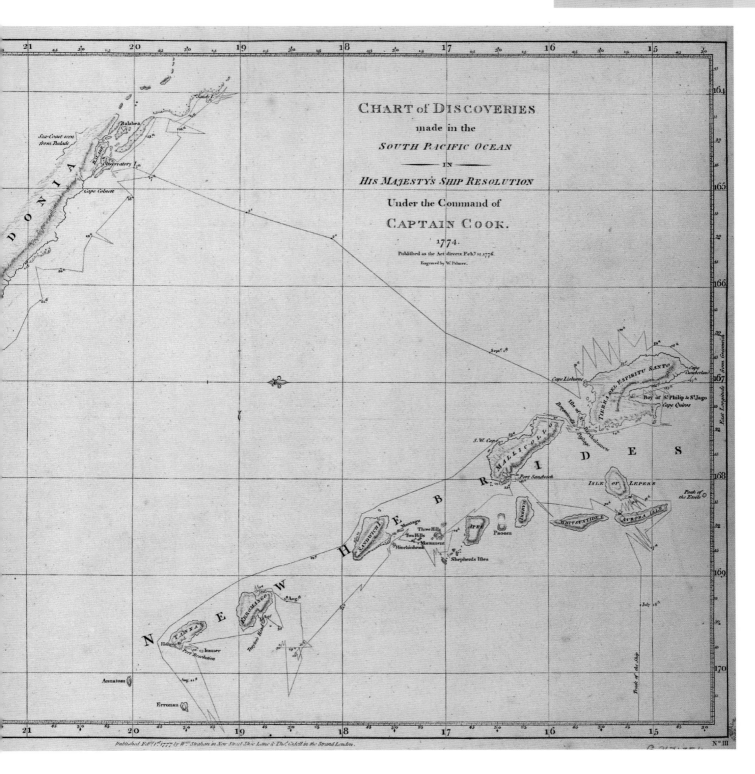

CHART of DISCOVERIES
made in the
SOUTH PACIFIC OCEAN
IN
HIS MAJESTY'S SHIP RESOLUTION
Under the Command of
CAPTAIN COOK.
1774.
Published as the Act directs Feb.y 12.1776.
Engraved by W. Palmer.

Opposite: *Cook hoped to locate the 'great southern continent' but found only iceberg-ridden seas and an inhospitable ice sheet.*

Above: *Cook explored and charted Pacific islands that were previously unknown to the British.*

James Douglas, Earl of Morton, president of the Royal Society between 1764 and 1768, described Cook's geographical achievements as having 'fixed the bounds of the navigable earth, as well as those of the navigable ocean, in the southern hemisphere.' Cook's cartographic successes were underpinned by the new methods available to him for calculating longitude as well as latitude, and the quality of the instruments he carried on board. On his first voyage, using the lunar distance method of calculating longitude, he was nonetheless able to create charts that were mostly accurate to within half a degree of longitude. On Cook's second voyage he carried a chronometer made to Harrison's design by watchmaker Larcum Kendall, which proved to be reliable, enabling Cook to draw on both methods to fix locations.

Captain Cook and the *Endeavour* sailors were highly privileged to have at their fingertips new navigational technology and methods for calculating longitude. Sailors at this time were still primarily reliant on calculating latitude only, and using knowledge and traditional navigational techniques that had been passed on down the centuries. It would take more than 100 years for timekeepers and methods for calculating longitude to become more widely used. Having a reliable means to pinpoint the position of both ships and terrestrial features did not automatically make sea travel safer, either. Uncharted rocks and bad weather continued to present dangers that enhanced navigation could not always overcome. The *Endeavour*, for example, almost sank after running aground on the Great Barrier Reef during Cook's first circumnavigation.

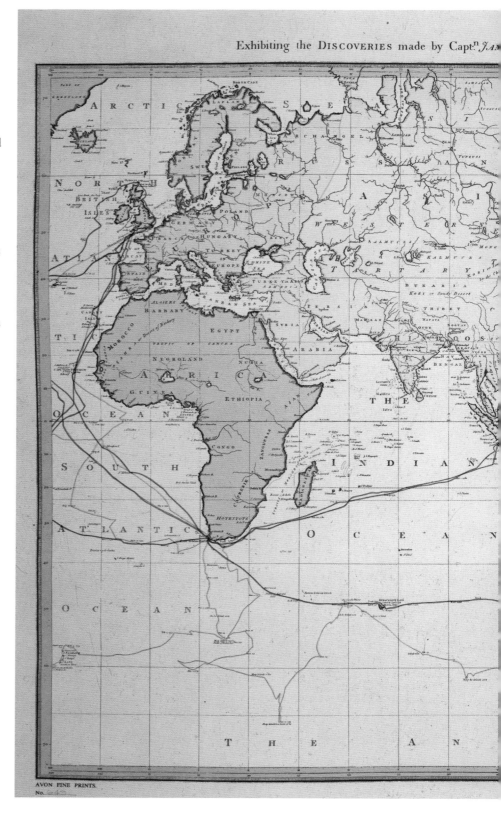

Exhibiting the DISCOVERIES made by Captn. JAM

AVON FINE PRINTS.
No.

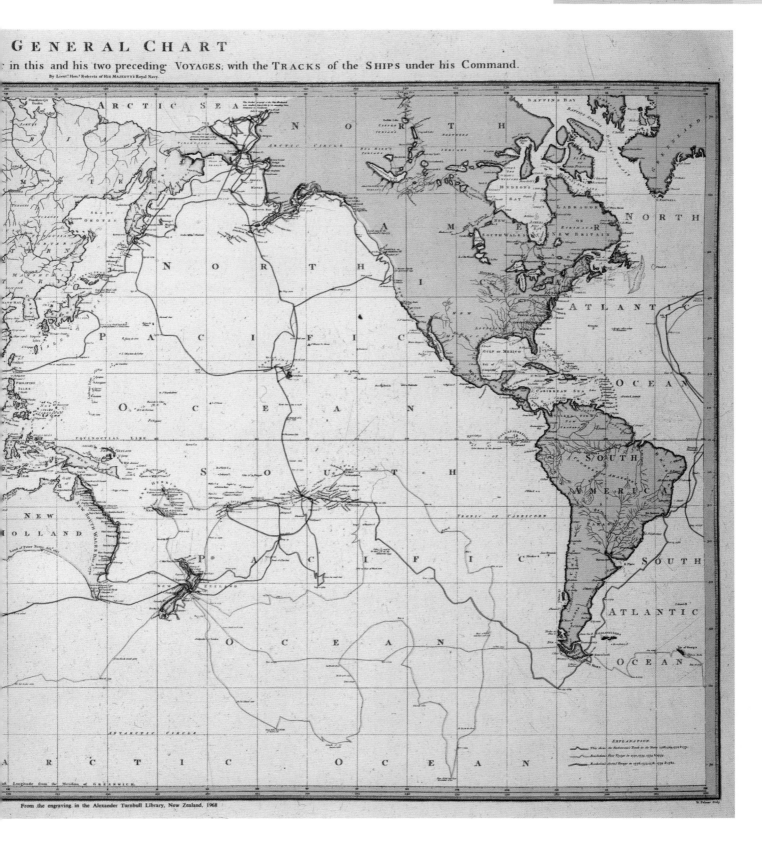

GENERAL CHART
in this and his two preceding VOYAGES; with the TRACKS of the SHIPS under his Command.
By Lieut.? Hen.? Roberts of His Majesty's Royal Navy.

From the engraving in the Alexander Turnbull Library, New Zealand, 1968

Above: *A map from 1785 showing the routes of Cook's three voyages.*

However, being able to reliably calculate longitude and latitude did mean that Cook was no longer limited to sailing at particular latitudes or hugging coastlines but could zigzag the Pacific without getting lost. And it meant that positions could now be tied to the invisible coordinate grid of longitude and latitude encircling the globe, instead of having to relate a new position to the ship's previous location, the distance from that place and the direction of travel from it. This not only enabled Cook to chart his expedition's own path and define the boundaries of land according to their position on the globe, but also meant that he could verify or dismiss location information provided by earlier explorers. In the long term, the ability to calculate longitude led to increased safety at sea by improving the quality of maps and charts. And it set the method for geometrically mapping coordinates of geographic features in two dimensions, which has continued to this day.

Endeavour's wreck close to being located

Cook's ship on the first circumnavigation, best known as *Endeavour*, was a barque built using 200 mature oak trees in Whitby, UK. Designed to carry coal, the vessel was initially named the *Earl of Pembroke*. However, when the British Navy bought it for Cook's expedition it was renamed *Endeavour* to reflect its new exploration role.

Following the voyage, the *Endeavour* was sold in 1775 to a private owner, and renamed the *Lord Sandwich*. The ship was used by the British Navy in the American War of Independence. In 1778, it was one of five ships scuttled at Rhode Island, New England, in an effort to block the French from joining American forces. Thirteen chartered transport vessels, including *Lord Sandwich*, were sunk along with warships.

Although the wreck of the ship is likely in Newport Harbour, it has not yet been located and officially identified. In 2018, a new document found in the British National Archives indicated that the *Lord Sandwich* was one of five vessels sunk in a particular part of the harbour. The Rhode Island Marine Archaeology Project subsequently reported it had narrowed the search to one or two archaeological sites, due for excavation in 2019.

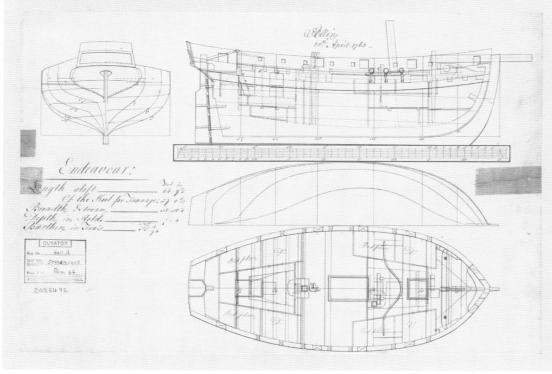

Left: *Plan of the* Endeavour.

LOCATING THE GREAT RIVER IN THE SEA

The presence of the great ocean current we now call the Gulf Stream was first recorded in 1513. The Spanish noble Juan Ponce de León had recently established a settlement on Puerto Rico, and was encouraged by the Spanish crown to look for other new lands. He organized an expedition from Puerto Rico to find an island known by locals as Bimini; in fact, he landed on the most south-easterly part of the North American continent, which he named *La Florida*. It was while sailing along the coast of this land that he and navigator Antón de Alaminos encountered 'such a current that, despite the strong wind, they did not advance but were seriously going backwards; finally it was concluded that the current was stronger than the wind.'

Within a few years, the Spanish were exploiting this current on journeys they made from South America to Europe, by sailing northwards along the Florida coastline before turning east. However, it was not until 1769–1770 that the Gulf Stream became widely publicized. By now, North America had been colonized by settlers from several European nations. Benjamin Franklin, who was General Manager of the Post of New England at the time, heard complaints that westbound mail from Europe took a couple of weeks longer to reach its destination than eastbound mail from America. He subsequently learned from his cousin Timothy Folger, a ship's captain and whaler, that English ships were hindered by the easterly flow of the Gulf Stream.

Below: *In the eighteenth century, packet ships regularly transported mail between British and American ports.*

Folger sketched out and annotated a map of the Gulf Stream, drawing on the knowledge of Nantucket whalers. Whaling had expanded in New England in the early eighteenth century in response to demand for whale products, such as oil for machinery and lighting. The sailors had observed that whales kept to the edge of the current, seeming to dislike its relatively warmer core. They had also often experienced the swift pace of the current; crews of smaller whaleboats despatched to chase down an animal often became quickly separated by it from the mother ship.

The whalers had verbally passed on their knowledge of the current to captains of American ships, enabling them to reduce the time of their eastbound journeys accordingly. Franklin had Folger's map engraved and distributed to English sea captains so that they might, too, speed up their journeys. However, they largely ignored the chart, preferring to take their shorter, but much slower, route. After the American Revolution began in 1775, Franklin gave the map to the French, which assisted them in shipping weapons to America.

Opposite: *Franklin and Timothy Folger drew on the knowledge of whalers to map the route of the Gulf Stream.*

Left: *Benjamin Franklin, who recognized that the Gulf Stream affected the speed of Atlantic journeys.*

A CHART of The GULF STREAM

James Poupard *sculp.*

Several observations of the current made over the years had noted the high temperature of the seawater within it. As early as 1606, the French author, lawyer and explorer Marc Lescarbot had recorded that: 'Six times twenty leagues to the eastward of the Banks of Newfoundland, we found for the space of three days the water very warm, whilst the air was cold as before, but on June 21 quite suddenly we were surrounded by fogs and cold that we thought to be in the month of January, and the sea was extremely cold.' When Franklin travelled between America and Europe he recorded the temperature of the water at set coordinates, observing that currents running north to south were colder than those flowing south to north. He concluded that temperature measurements could help ships to navigate the Atlantic. His nephew Jonathan Williams embraced this idea, continuing to take measurements after Franklin's last voyage and publishing, in 1799, the book *Thermometrical Navigation*.

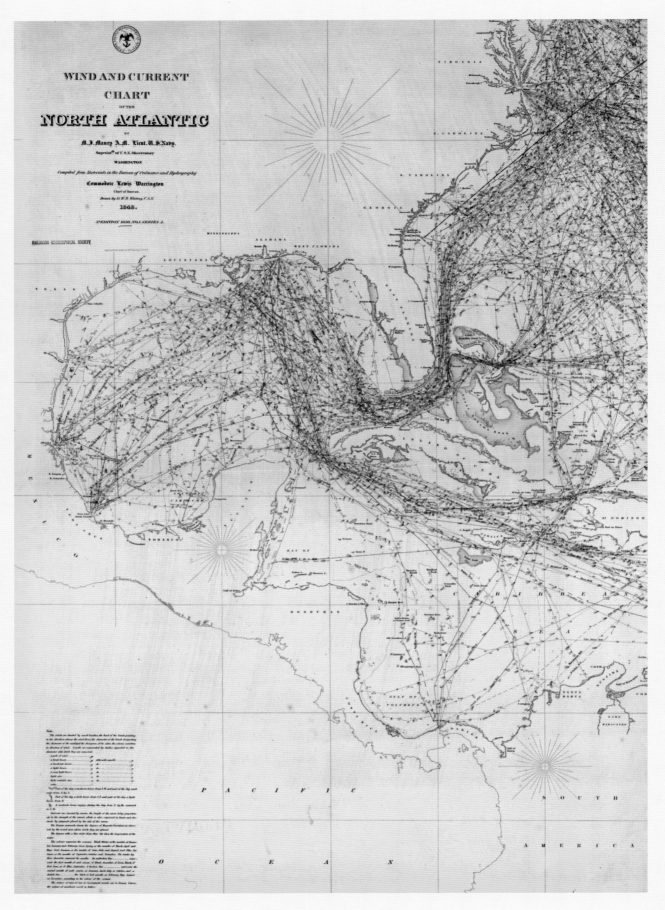

Above: *Matthew Fontaine Maury's wind and current chart of the Atlantic.*

Above: *British geographer James Rennell.*

Below: *Merchant vessels like this clipper accumulated important data during their Atlantic crossings, which was used by Maury to produce wind and current charts.*

Two pioneering geographers built on Franklin's and Williams' scientific work, in the process helping to launch the field of physical oceanography. Both drew on the rich source of information on ocean currents provided by ships' logbooks.

In Britain, the geographer Major James Rennell spent his retirement generating charts of Atlantic currents, focusing on the Gulf Stream. He drew on current and weather observations collected by the British Admiralty. Rennell's efforts were published in 1832, two years after he died, in *An investigation of the currents of the Atlantic Ocean, and of those which prevail between the Indian Ocean and the Atlantic*. Presenting information such as the pattern and variability of currents, prevailing winds in relation to the current flow, sea depths and temperatures, it was the first comprehensive scientific report on the Gulf Stream.

On the other side of the Atlantic, Matthew Fontaine Maury generated wind and current charts of the Atlantic, Pacific and Indian Oceans. Maury drew on data from ships' logs stored at the US Navy's Depot of Charts and Instruments, where he worked as superintendent. These charts proved highly useful to mariners, who used them to aid navigation. The information was also helpful in cutting the sailing times of some merchant vessels, saving money for their operators. Maury instigated the first international conference on meteorology in 1853, which led to international cooperation on data collection on board ships crossing the Atlantic. The culmination of Maury's work was published in *The Physical Geography of the Sea and its Meteorology* in 1856.

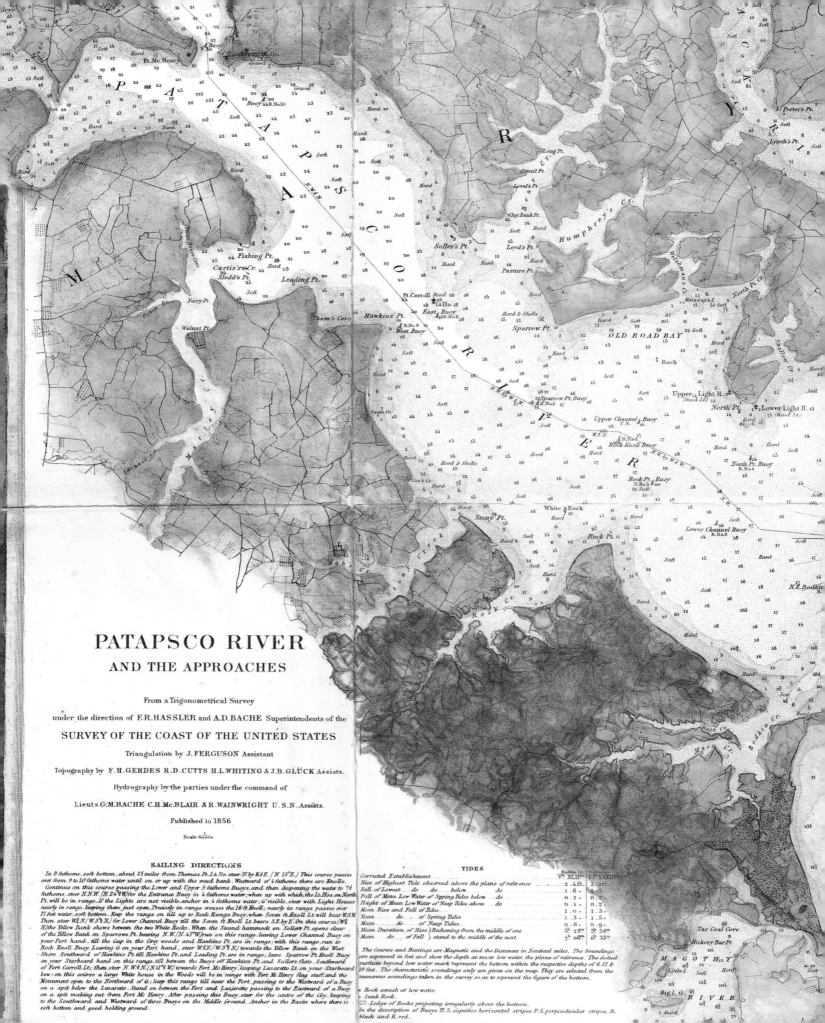

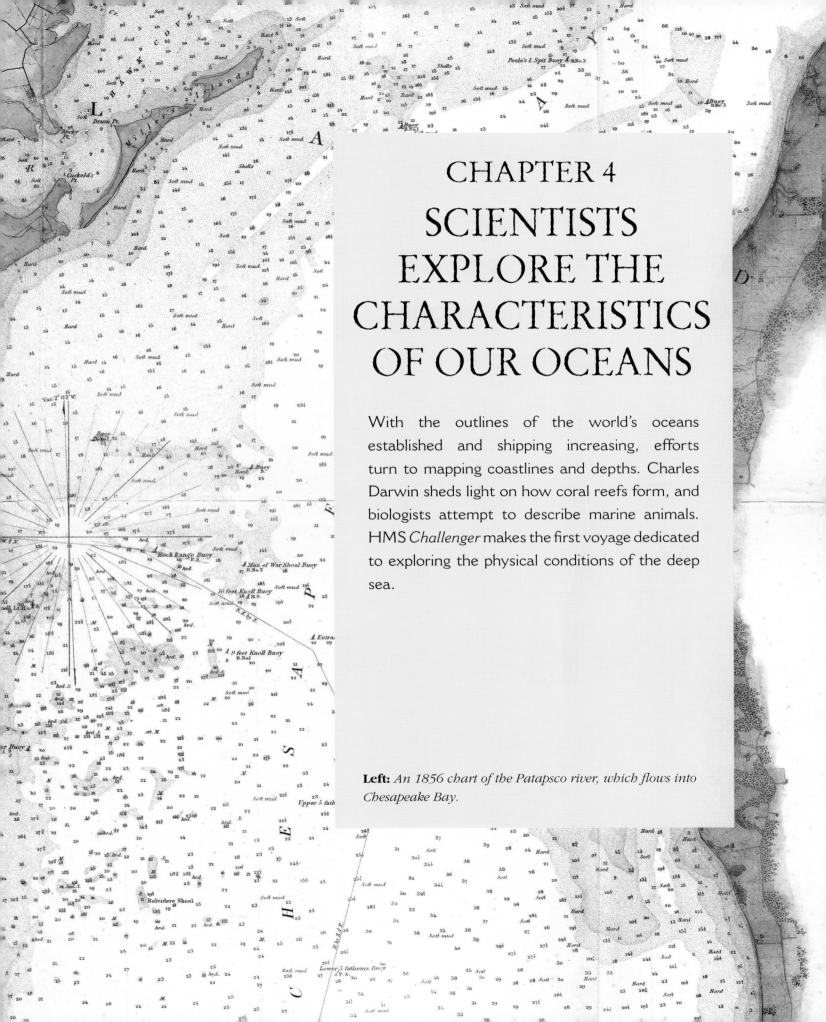

CHAPTER 4
SCIENTISTS EXPLORE THE CHARACTERISTICS OF OUR OCEANS

With the outlines of the world's oceans established and shipping increasing, efforts turn to mapping coastlines and depths. Charles Darwin sheds light on how coral reefs form, and biologists attempt to describe marine animals. HMS *Challenger* makes the first voyage dedicated to exploring the physical conditions of the deep sea.

Left: *An 1856 chart of the Patapsco river, which flows into Chesapeake Bay.*

SURVEYING OF COASTLINES AND THE DEEP GETS UNDER WAY

Britain and America chart the Atlantic Ocean

In the first half of the eighteenth century, the French proved Isaac Newton's theory that Earth was not a perfect sphere but was flattened at the poles. They did this by demonstrating that one degree of a longitudinal meridian was longer in Lapland than in Paris. This paved the way for surveyors to locate and relate features on the Earth's surface to each other, while correcting for the planet's size, shape and gravity. By 1800, most European countries had begun undertaking such 'geodetic surveys' by establishing triangulation networks. This method of large-scale land surveying remained valid until superseded by global navigation satellite systems in the 1980s.

As shipping expanded in the early nineteenth century, Britain and America developed active programmes to create charts of

Above: *Prior to the Battle of Trafalgar, depicted here, Thomas Atkinson, Master of HMS* Victory *under Admiral Horatio Nelson, carried French charts, as British ones were not available.*

Left: *Alexander Dalrymple, first Hydrographer to the Admiralty, helped to get Britain's hydrographic effort off the ground.*

domestic, colonial and foreign ports. Britain's Hydrographic Office was founded in 1795, with Alexander Dalrymple appointed as the first Hydrographer to the Admiralty. Up to this point, the British Navy had produced no charts of its own, and even those generated on expeditions sponsored by the Admiralty, such as Captain Cook's, were published by commercial map publishers. The hope was that the Office would help England to gain 'her rightful place in chart-making among the maritime nations of the world'.

Dalrymple began work by organizing the Admiralty's library of existing charts. This meant that the first map produced by the Hydrographic Office (of Quiberon Bay, Brittany, France) was not published until 1800. In fact, Thomas Atkinson, Master of HMS *Victory* under Admiral Horatio Nelson would carry French charts when navigating the Mediterranean in the lead-up to the Battle of Trafalgar in 1805.

Thereafter, however, the Office's map-making gathered pace. Regular surveys were undertaken and 'sailing directions' produced (providing information to guide sailors in coastal and port areas). For the first time, maps were made available to the public and merchant navy. By 1825, the Hydrographic Office was able to list 736 charts in its first Admiralty catalogue.

Soon, the Office began systematically surveying areas deemed to be of particular commercial, colonial or strategic importance. Surveys of note included the 1839–43 British Naval Expedition led by James Clark Ross and Francis Crozier (which sought to conduct magnetic observations in the southern hemisphere and locate the South Magnetic Pole) and Fitzroy's 1831–36 voyage in HMS *Beagle* to survey the coast of South America. By 1855, the Admiralty map catalogue had swelled to 1,981 charts.

Below: *HMS* Beagle's *1831–36 survey of South America was ordered by the British Hydrographic Office.*

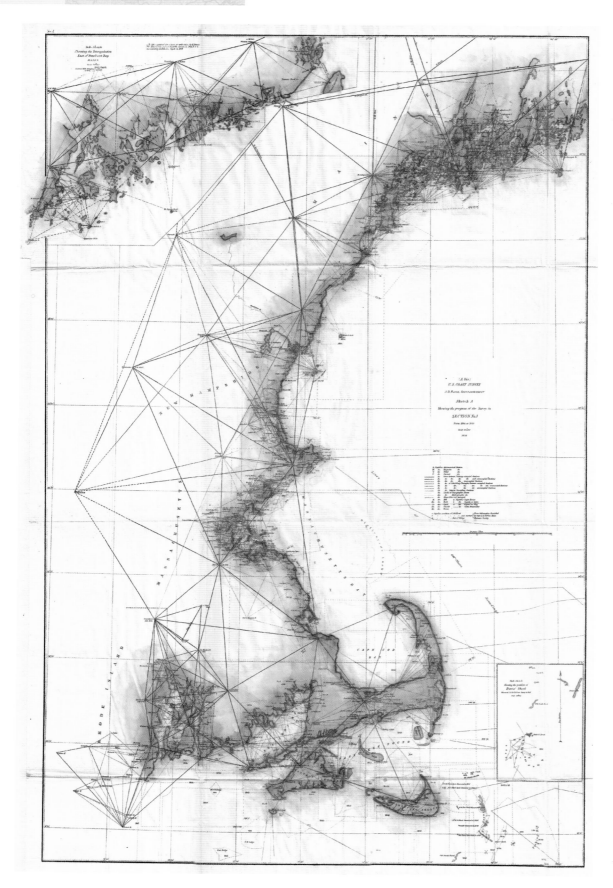

On the other side of the Atlantic, similar surveying efforts also got under way in the early nineteenth century. In 1807, United States President Thomas Jefferson signed legislation 'to cause a survey to be taken of the coasts of the United States, in which shall be designated the islands and shoals, with the roads or places of anchorage, within twenty leagues of any part of the shores of the United States; and also the respective courses and distances between the principal capes, or head lands [sic], together with such other matters as he may deem proper for completing an accurate chart of every part of the coasts within the extent aforesaid.'

The purpose was to ensure the safe passage of people and goods by ship, at a time when shipwrecks were all too common. At this point, the coast of the United States extended from New Hampshire to Georgia, but the survey also encompassed the recently purchased Louisiana Territory. Ferdinand Rudolph Hassler, a Swiss mathematician and surveyor, lead the survey. He aimed to build a geodetic triangulation network as a framework for topographic surveys of the shoreline and hydrographic surveys of harbours and offshore waters.

After a slow start caused by a delay in obtaining precision instruments, a survey of New York Harbour got under way in 1816. However, Hassler was dismissed soon after and the agency passed into military hands, with all operations suspended. The Survey of the Coast was re-established in 1832 with Hassler as its superintendent. By now, the coastal states of Mississippi, Alabama and Maine were also part of the Union, and the USA coastline stretched for some 40,784 km (25,342 miles).

In triangulation surveying, a baseline is established and then angles calculated from each end of this line to a visible third point, creating a triangle of three known points. Hassler used this method to establish a network of reference points on land. He then mapped the shoreline at multiple water levels to determine times and heights of high and low tides. Offshore, depth soundings were taken using a simple weighted line. Initially, just a few assistants supported Hassler but by 1842 the organization had numerous land field parties engaged in surveying.

Such was Hassler's diligence, it took 20 years to complete this process for New York Harbour alone. However, undertaking the survey revealed a new deep-water channel into the harbour, proving the value of the work. The charts were published in 1845, two years after Hassler's death. The surveying principles employed by Hassler and his team underpinned the majority of coastal surveying conducted in the nineteenth century and beyond.

Hassler was succeeded by Alexander Dallas Bache, a great-grandson of Benjamin Franklin. By now, Texas and Florida had joined the Union (in 1845) and were soon followed (in 1850) by California. The addition of these states added thousands of square miles of territory to the USA, including extensive coastlines along the Pacific Ocean and Gulf of Mexico. The availability of land attracted thousands of immigrants to the States from Europe throughout the nineteenth century. Many came to take advantage of the Homesteader Act, which offered 160 acres of land free for anyone agreeing to till it for five years. The population stood at more than 17 million in 1840, exceeded 31 million in 1860 and topped 76 million in 1900.

The swelling population provided labour for America's industrial revolution, and the development of industries such as coal and steel. Cities expanded, including those on the coast; New Orleans quickly grew to become the fourth largest port in the world. The expansion of maritime commerce and new technologies led to the development of the first clippers, and later steamships. These helped to speed up ocean journeys and facilitated the global movement of people and goods.

Bache embraced the surveying challenges that this shifting maritime landscape presented. Within his first four years in the job, he expanded the Survey from operating in nine states to working in 16, and extended its remit to encompass geophysics. Potentially influenced by his great-grandfather, he also set about investigating characteristics of the Gulf Stream, such as temperature, depth, bottom character, direction and velocity of currents, and life forms. And, as the science of tidal prediction evolved (see box opposite), he established tidal stations and published the Survey's first tide tables, from 1855. By the time Bache died in 1867, he had built the Survey into one of the premier surveying institutions in the world.

Above: *Ports such as New Orleans, seen here, grew rapidly as immigrants arrived in America to start new lives.*

Learning to predict tides

People have been thinking about the causes of tidal movement, and how to measure and predict tides, for thousands of years. The Greek astronomer and explorer Pytheas was the first known to note, around 300 BCE, that there are two tides a day and that the amplitude of these tides depends on the phases of the moon.

Much later, in 1687, Isaac Newton realized that gravitation lay behind tidal movements. This led natural philosophers to use mathematics to unravel the complexities of tides. The French mathematician and astronomer Pierre-Simon, Marquis de Laplace, made an important contribution to knowledge in the late-eighteenth and early-nineteenth centuries, realizing that tides could be mathematically separated into three types: long periodical (gravitational tides with periods of more than one day), diurnal and semi-diurnal (with periods of a day or less). This became a cornerstone of tidal theory. Data on tide heights and times, collected as surveying efforts gathered pace in the nineteenth century, helped underpin further research.

Once scientists fully understood the complex mathematics of tidal movements – including the influence of 'Earth tides' – they were able to create the first tide-prediction machines. Based on the principle of harmonic analysis – in which constituent tides (the long periodical, diurnal and semi-diurnal) represented by harmonic constants are combined into a composite tides – these were essentially analogue computers simulating the rise and fall of ocean tides. Various machines were developed in the UK, USA and Germany between 1872 and 1964.

During the D-Day landings of 1944, a tide-predicting machine helped the Allies exploit an exceptionally high and rising tide that carried their landing craft safely over tank traps and other obstacles. The Germans had hoped the traps would force the troops to land lower down the beach, making them an easy target for snipers. From 1965, digital electronic computers took over the role of making tidal predictions. Today, anyone planning to spend a day at the beach can check online in seconds when high and low tide will occur.

Above: *A tide-predicting machine.*

Left: *The D-Day landings were timed to coincide with an exceptionally high tide.*

Revealing the mysteries of the deep

While the world's coastlines and shallows were slowly coming into sharper focus in the early nineteenth century, the deep seas remained an enigma. A common perception in Europe was that they were empty and featureless; the antithesis of civilization. By around the middle of the nineteenth century, however, the seashore was becoming popular as a place for reflection and pleasure. This, coupled with the seafaring experiences of emigrants, maritime workers, and travelling artists and writers, helped to focus attention on deeper waters.

The earliest efforts to systematically record ocean depths were conducted on polar voyages. Sir John Ross recorded a depth of 1,000 fathoms (1 fathom = six feet, or 1.8 metres) on his 1817–18 expedition to search for a seaway through the Arctic (the so-called Northwest Passage); while, on the British Naval Expedition in 1840, his nephew James Ross measured depths of 2,425 and 2,677 fathoms, with no depth recorded on two attempts made with 4,000 fathoms of line reeled out.

Opposite: *Sir John Ross, an explorer and early recorder of ocean characteristics in the Arctic.*

Below: *HMS* Erebus *and HMS* Terror *during the British Naval Expedition of 1839, on which James Ross recorded an ocean depth of 2,677 fathoms.*

In the United States, the US Depot of Charts and Instruments was established in 1830 to look after the Department of the Navy's chronometers, charts and other navigational equipment. When Matthew Fontaine Maury took over as director in 1842, he spied an opportunity for the organization to investigate the deeper offshore waters that were beyond the remit of the US Coast Survey. According to Maury: 'the bottom of what the sailors called "blue water" was as unknown to us as is the interior of any of the planets of our system.'

Early efforts by Maury to expand knowledge of the oceans focused more on 'dismissing shallow waters' rather than charting the depths. Often, mariners traversing deep waters reported the presence of 'vigias', exposed rocks or shoals that could present a hazard to shipping. Maury sent hydrographers to check these sightings and either locate them or disprove their existence. Confirming the absence of shallows helped to open up new shipping routes in areas previously considered as dangerous.

Maury later supported the 1853–56 North Pacific Exploring Expedition, which conducted ocean studies around the Arctic and in the Pacific. During the expedition, John Mercer Brooke, who had invented a detachable sounding device for obtaining samples of sea floor materials, took the first confirmed deep-sea soundings in the Pacific. These generally recorded depths of between 2,000 and 3,000 fathoms. Meanwhile, marine zoologist William Stimpson collected and studied fish and marine invertebrates.

The official scientific reports of the expedition were never published – possibly because the science of studying the depths and the creatures inhabiting them had yet to coalesce into a united field of study. However, both American and British hydrographers adopted Brooke's sounder. Thereafter, the practice of gathering seafloor samples and depth measurements together was widely adopted.

Right: *Zoologist William Stimpson described fish and marine invertebrates he encountered on the North Pacific Exploring Expedition.*

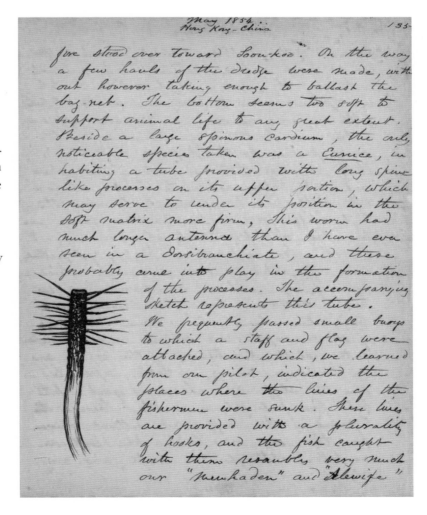

The development of submarine telegraphy provided a commercial and political stimulus for further research into the ocean depths. As early as 1839 the idea was mooted for a cable spanning the Atlantic. By 1851, the first submarine telegraph cable was in place and operational between France and England. And in the following few years, more cables were laid connecting various locations in Europe and Scandinavia.

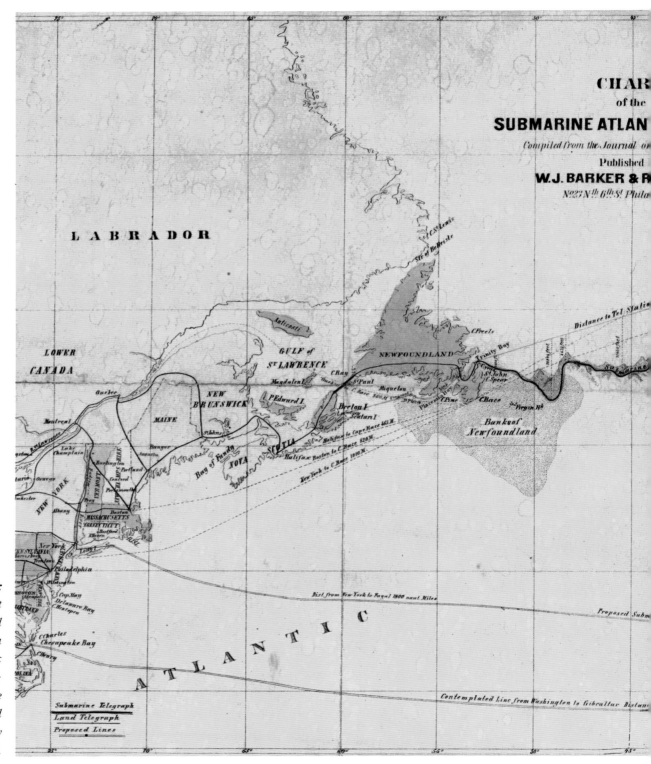

Right:
Engineers first attempted to lay a transatlantic cable in 1857; another nine years passed before they succeeded.

None of these achievements matched the scale of the desired transatlantic connection, however. The longest submarine cable operating in 1857, when engineers first attempted to connect America to Europe, was 177 km (110 miles) long and around 300 fathoms deep. Spanning the Atlantic called for a cable 3,200 km (2,000 miles) long to be laid in water some 2,500 fathoms deep.

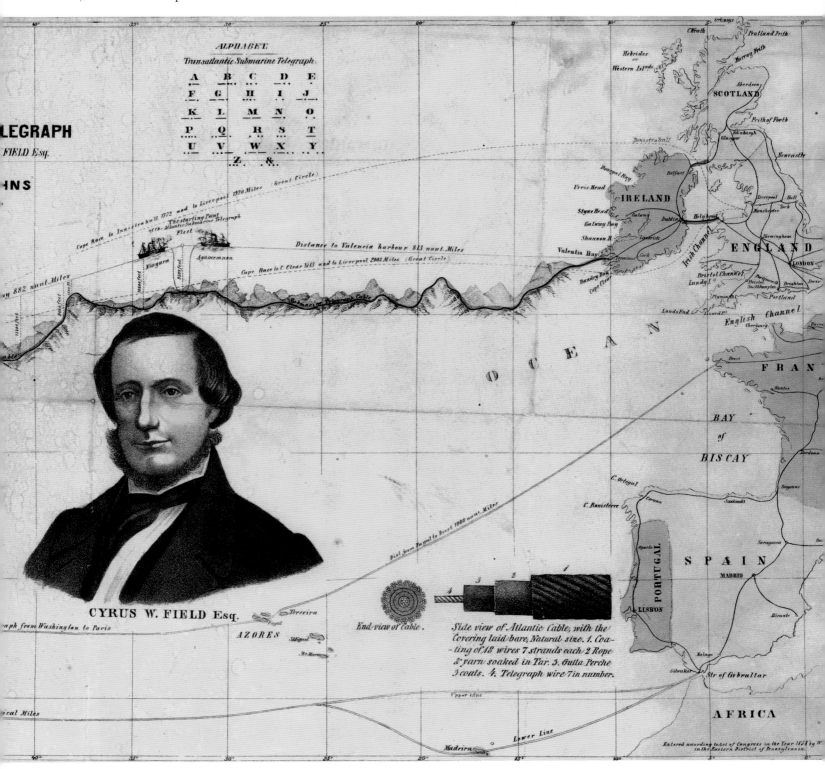

Submarine cables more important than ever

The core of the 1866 transatlantic cable comprised seven twisted copper strands, coated in a waterproof adhesive and sealed with four layers of gutta-percha (a form of inert and non-conductive latex derived from the sap of the tropical *Palaquium* tree). This was shrouded in preservative-soaked hemp and finally wrapped in steel wire covered with rope that was also soaked in preservative.

Modern cables, such as those used in Google's telecommunications infrastructure, comprise glass fibres coated in coloured plastics, with a Kevlar-like protective outer layer. A strong outer coating is vital, as sharks have been reported to attack underwater cables.

Today, some 430 submarine cables are in service, totalling 1,100,000 km (683,508 miles) in length. Although local wireless networks suggest that physical infrastructure is less important in the modern age, this is not the case. In fact, submarine cables transmit 99 per cent of all telecommunications traffic between continents, including data, texts, emails and phone calls.

In 2018 a new transatlantic cable known as the Marea cable (*Marea* is Spanish for tide) became operational between Virginia Beach, USA and Bilbao, Spain. In an experiment, one of its eight pairs of fibre-optic cables achieved a record data-transfer speed of 26.2 TBps (Terabytes per second), although current average transfer rates are 9.5 TBps. The cable was installed in a joint venture by Telxius, Facebook and Microsoft to help meet increasing demand for connections to the Cloud.

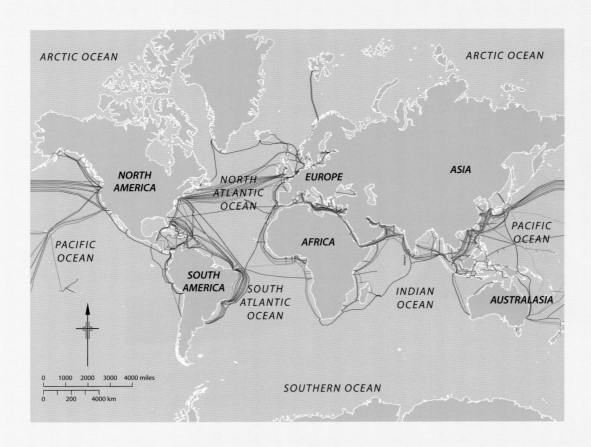

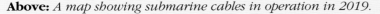

Above: *A map showing submarine cables in operation in 2019.*

The first attempt to lay a cable from Ireland to Newfoundland failed when the cable broke. The second, a year later, was initially successful, but the cable failed after one month. It was seven years before a third attempt was made, which was also unsuccessful. Only in 1866 was a cable laid that endured. It had been reeled out from the world's largest ship afloat at the time – the *Great Eastern* – between Valentia Island, Ireland, and Newfoundland, Canada.

Cable technology had improved considerably since the first attempt. Whereas it had taken more than 17 hours to transmit the first 509-letter message sent in 1858, the 1866 cable could transmit eight words per minute. This meant that people in Europe and North America could communicate with each other almost simultaneously.

As telegraph technology and laying methods improved, subsea cables proliferated. By the early twentieth century, much of the world was connected. Information could now be disseminated quickly between governments, businesses and the public. After the invention of the telephone in 1875, phone lines, too began to link continents via submarine cables. And in the late 1980s, the first transoceanic fibre-optic cable was laid. Today, around 430 submarine cables continue to connect locations around the world (see box opposite).

Above: *The end of the first successful transatlantic cable emerging at the shore in Ireland in 1866.*

DARWIN'S CORAL REEF THEORY STANDS THE TEST OF TIME

Years before Charles Darwin published his theory of evolution in *On the Origin of Species*, he developed another, equally enduring, hypothesis on the formation of coral reefs. Darwin outlined his opinions in his first scientific book *The Structure and Distribution of Coral Reefs*, published in 1842. As with *Origin*, Darwin's ideas on coral-reef formation took shape during his journey on HMS *Beagle* between 1831 and 1836. At odds with the most widely accepted reef theory of the time, it prompted much debate during the nineteenth century but was eventually proven to be largely correct in the early 1950s.

While aboard the *Beagle*, Darwin had eagerly read the first two volumes of Charles Lyell's *Principles of Geology*. He enthused about Lyell's approach to nature, which dismissed the idea of Earth being shaped by God-driven cataclysmic events in favour of its features forming slowly over time by steady and ongoing natural processes. Darwin's belief in Lyell's perspective was crystallized when he witnessed geology in

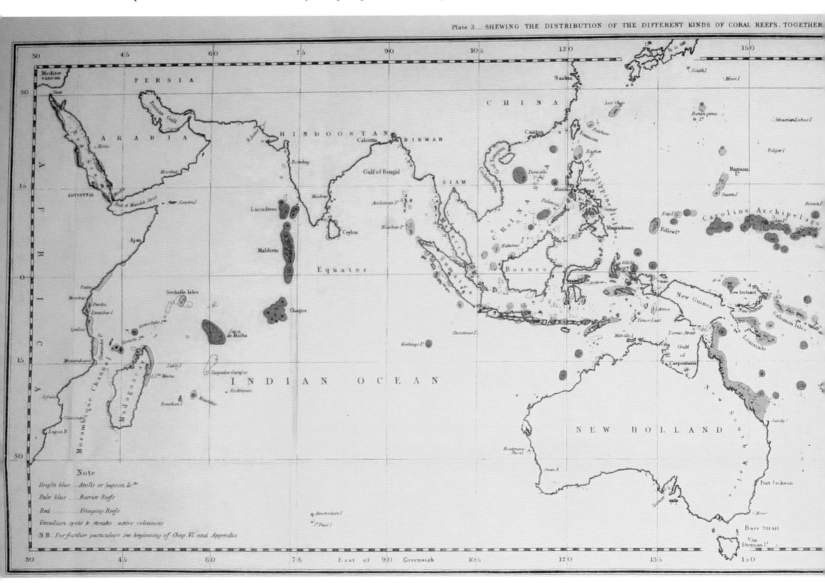

Above: *Charles Darwin's 1842 map showing the distribution of coral reefs and active volcanoes in the Pacific and Indian Oceans.*

action while the *Beagle* was travelling north along the coast of Chile. In January of 1835 he observed Mount Osorno erupting, and then, one month later, he experienced a major earthquake.

Where Darwin disagreed with Lyell was on how coral reefs formed in the Pacific. The widely accepted theory at that time, which Lyell promoted in the second volume of *Principles*, was that 'lagoon islands' (coral atolls) were 'nothing more than the crests of submarine volcanoes, having the rims and bottoms of their craters overgrown by corals.' Scientists already knew that reef-building corals inhabited only shallow water. This theory proposed that coral reefs grew on volcanoes that had risen under the sea close to the surface. It accounted for the ring-like shape of reefs as well as providing a way for reefs to grow in Pacific waters that would otherwise have been far too deep for corals.

By the time Darwin traversed the west coast of South America, and before even seeing his first coral reef, he had developed an alternative theory. He saw with his own eyes that molluscs, barnacles and other sea life were pushed up out of the water by the earthquake he had experienced. And he observed seashells and coral at various

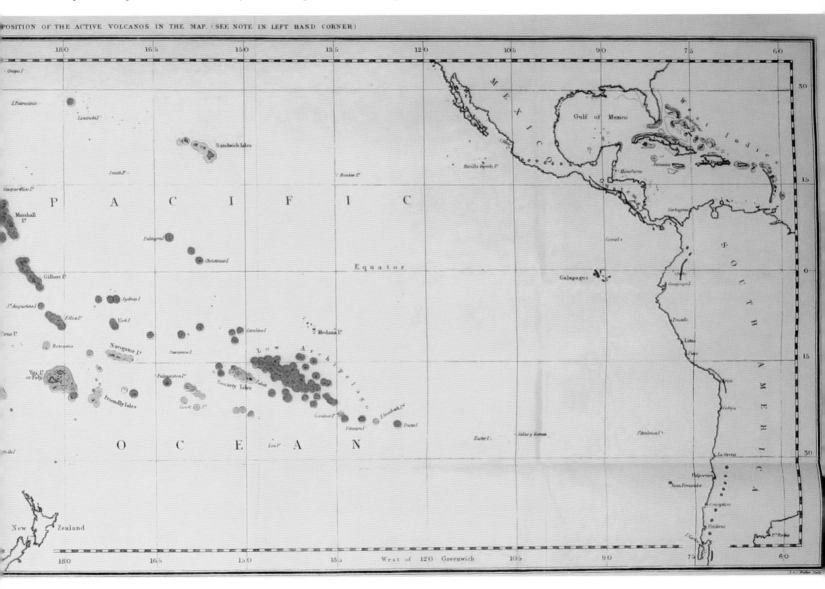

heights in different locations, the highest located at an altitude of 3,660 m (12,000 ft) in the Andes. He concluded that land was being lifted by 'successive small uprisings, such as that which accompanied or caused the earthquake', and also by oceanic volcanoes. He identified the driver of these movements as a layer of molten rock below the Earth's crust.

Darwin reasoned that the uplift he observed on land might be compensated for by subsidence in the oceans; this, he felt, could explain the location and appearance of coral reefs. He agreed that live reef-building corals thrived only in shallow water, and that they appeared to be associated with seamounts or submerged volcanoes. However, Darwin hypothesized that different types of reefs formed sequentially as the landmasses from which they grew slowly subsided. Initially, a fringing reef would lie around an island's shores. As the land on which the reef grew slowly sank, this would give rise to a barrier reef, with a deep lagoon separating the reef from the shore. When the island sank completely, an atoll – a circular reef enclosing a deep lagoon – would result.

Above: *Geologist Charles Lyell had proposed an alternative hypothesis of coral reef evolution but was won over to Darwin's theory.*

When the *Beagle* sailed west across the Pacific to Tahiti and later on to the Indian Ocean Cocos (Keeling) Islands, Darwin was finally able to inspect barrier reefs and atolls at close hand. His observations of these structures, which beguiled him, convinced him that his theory was right. Of the Cocos (Keeling) Islands, he wrote: 'I am glad we have visited these Islands; such formations surely rank high amongst the wonderful objects of this world. It is not a wonder which at first strikes the eye of the body, but rather after reflection, the eye of reason.' And referring to islands in the Pacific, including Tahiti and Eimeo, he declared: 'we must look at a Lagoon Isd

Fig. 102.—Structure of Coral-reefs.　1. Fringing-reef ; 2. Barrier-reef ; 3. Atoll.　*a* Sea-level ; *b* Coral-reef ; *c* Primitive land ; *d* Portion of sea within the reef, forming a channel or lagoon.

Above: *Darwin's theory of how coral reefs form.*

as a monument raised by myriads of tiny architects, to mark the spot where a former land lies in the depths of the ocean.'

When Darwin told Lyell of his theory shortly after returning to England in 1836, Lyell embraced it, quickly discarding his own former opinion that reefs grew on top of mountains that had risen up through the ocean. It seemed obvious that if coral grew on something that was rising from the seas, the coral would die as soon as it was elevated above the water. On land that was sinking, a living crust of coral could thrive atop older coral foundations by growing upwards towards the sunlight. After reading an abstract of his theory at the Geological Society in London, and publishing his monograph *The Structure and Distribution of Coral Reefs*, Darwin won over other eminent scientists. By 1850 the hypothesis had become widely accepted, but the debate opened up again in the later nineteenth century when alternative theories were put forward.

It took almost a century from publication for Darwin's hypothesis to be scientifically evaluated. In the early 1950s, ahead of testing nuclear bombs on a remote coral atoll in the Marshall Islands, the US government arranged for cores to be drilled. The geophysicists penetrated 1,280 m (4,200 ft) of coral before reaching a greenish layer of volcanic basalt; the base on which the coral had formed. When the bottommost layer of coral was dated, scientists realized it had been growing for 30 million years, inching its way upwards towards the light as the volcano beneath it slowly subsided. Darwin had been right.

Below:

Investigations of Bikini atoll in the 1950s proved Darwin's theory of coral formation to be correct.

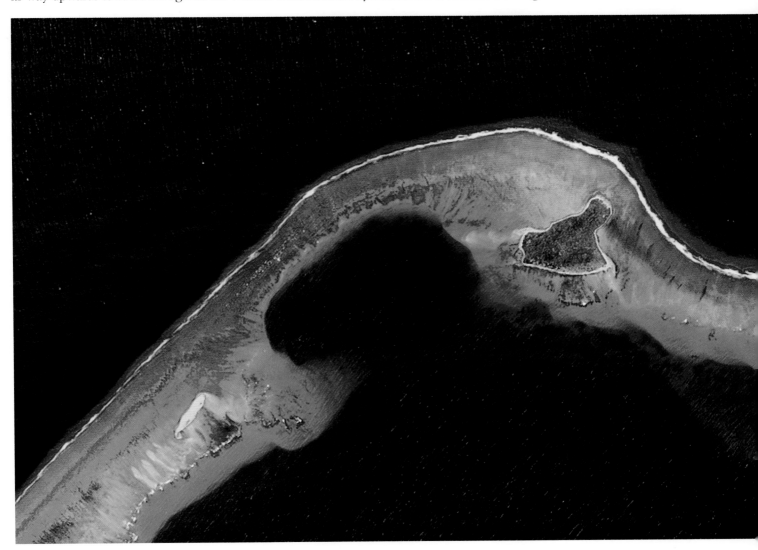

SEARCHING FOR LIFE IN THE OCEANS

As late as the mid-nineteenth century, knowledge of the creatures inhabiting Earth's ocean depths was minimal. Although more people than ever were now working in the maritime industries and experiencing life at sea on journeys for migration and pleasure, opportunities for investigating what might live beneath the surface remained limited. Slowly, however, knowledge of sea creatures gleaned by fishermen for thousands of years was supplemented by the observations of naturalists exploring beaches and shallows, and through organisms brought to the surface by scientists in dredging hauls and during deep-sea soundings.

The well-regarded British naturalist Edward Forbes explored coastal waters around Greece and Turkey from the surveying vessel HMS *Beacon* in 1841. Working with scientists on board, Forbes dredged at depths down to 230 fathoms and noted that, with increasing depth, sea animals became less abundant. By extrapolation, he concluded that there would be 'zero of animal life probably about 300 fathoms'. He published his theory in the 1843 paper *Report on the Mollusca and Radiata of the Aegean Sea*. In it he identified eight depth-defined regions that were characterized by the fauna inhabiting them.

At the time it seemed reasonable that the great pressures, cold temperatures and darkness encountered in the deep would prevent life there. Most naturalists soon concurred with Forbes' theory, despite the fact that some earlier expeditions had reported finding organisms existing below this boundary (including deep-sea specimens observed in the Caribbean as early as 1761 and a basket star brought up from the depths on Ross's 1817–18 expedition). It was not until 1860, when a malfunctioning telegraph cable connecting Sardinia and Algeria was raised – and found to be encrusted with marine organisms – that the tide of opinion began to change. The base of one coral, of the genus *Caryophyllia*, was moulded to the cable, illustrating that the organism had lived for a considerable time at 1,200 fathoms.

Above: *British naturalist Edward Forbes proposed that no life existed in oceans below around 300 fathoms.*

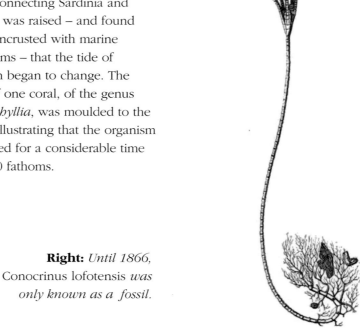

Right: *Until 1866,* Conocrinus lofotensis *was only known as a fossil.*

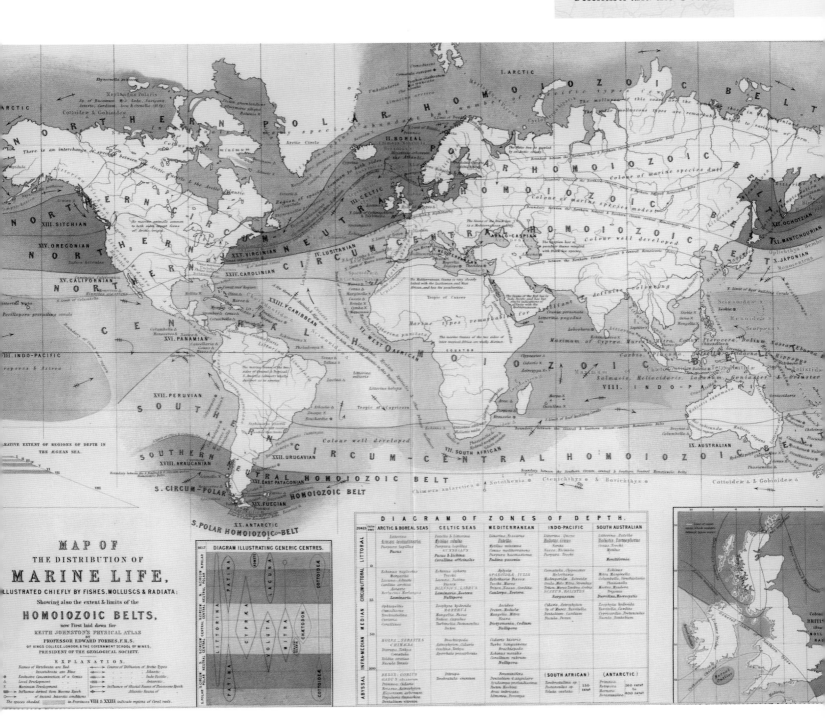

Above: *The geographical and vertical distribution of marine life, according to Edward Forbes.*

This incontrovertible proof that a deep-sea fauna existed made scientists want to know more. An important contributor to knowledge of deep-sea life around this time was Georg Ossian Sars, a superintendent of Norwegian fisheries, who compiled reports of the diverse animals he encountered at depths down to 450 fathoms. One find particularly fascinated scientists. In 1866, Sars dredged a stalked crinoid from 300 fathoms down in a spot close to the Lofoten Islands. This kind of crinoid, which is now known as *Conocrinus lofotensis,* had previously been encountered only in the fossil record. With Darwin's theory on evolution through natural selection not long published, scientists embraced the idea that the deep oceans might be repositories for 'living fossils'.

One scientist inspired by Sars was Charles Wyville Thomson, a Scottish naturalist and marine zoologist. He urged his colleague William Benjamin Carpenter, a physiologist-turned-marine zoologist and Royal Society Council member, to assist him in trying to secure Admiralty support for a new expedition to survey life in the deep ocean. Sars' specimens, he wrote, 'place it beyond a doubt that animal life is abundant in the ocean at depths varying from 200 fathoms [1,200 ft] to 300 fathoms [1,800 ft].' Carpenter duly wrote to the president of the Royal Society, which led the Admiralty to provide funds and the ship HMS *Lightning*.

Despite 'deplorable weather' and the fact that the ship 'kept out the water imperfectly', the *Lightning* expedition spent six weeks in 1868 successfully dredging and taking temperature measurements in waters between Shetland and the Faroe Islands. The scientists' success was underpinned by new sounding technology, which was operated by a steam engine and incorporated india-rubber accumulators to prevent the line from breaking if the ship was thrown around in rough seas.. Dredging at 650 fathoms, almost double the depth of previous attempts, yielded diverse and numerous marine specimens. The scientists also discovered that water temperatures did not simply vary according to latitude as had been thought, but that discrete water bodies with distinct temperature profiles

Above: *Charles Wyville Thomson helped initiate expeditions to explore the oceans.*

followed their own courses within the sea. The results were so encouraging, the Admiralty agreed to provide HMS *Porcupine* for a four-month follow-up expedition.

This time, the focus was widened to investigate both zoological and physical aspects of the ocean. During a successful first leg in 1870, the researchers retrieved from 1,476 fathoms a haul that included molluscs, a stalk-eyed crustacean and a sea cucumber. They subsequently decided, for the second leg, to try dredging at the greatest depth in the vicinity, an area of around 2,500 fathoms west of Ushant, France, in the Bay of Biscay. A dredge at 2,435 fathoms brought up sediments containing fresh shells of *Globigerina,* and a variety of other animals. Clearly the deep oceans provided very favourable conditions for life.

Left: *The HMS* Porcupine *expedition of 1870 drew animals such as sea cucumbers up from the deep.*

Left: *Dredging for sea life on board HMS* Porcupine.

For the third leg of the expedition, the researchers continued dredging in shallower waters and undertook temperature and chemical measurements of warm and cold areas they had identified on the *Lightning* survey. After the ship's return, Carpenter was able to report that temperature was more likely than pressure to influence how marine creatures were distributed in the oceans. Two more surveys – one on HMS *Porcupine* in 1870 and another on HMS *Shearwater* in 1871 – revealed more about the oceanic fauna, as well as enabling scientists to start investigating the role of water density in driving ocean currents.

Within three decades, human understanding of what lay beneath the surface of the oceans had expanded considerably, to incorporate zoology, physics and chemistry. But with each question that was answered, more arose. What was needed, felt Wyville Thomson and Carpenter, was a longer, more ambitious expedition to systematically investigate the biological, geological, geographical, physical and chemical characteristics of oceans around the world. When Carpenter approached the Admiralty for support, it agreed, saying that 'science and navigation' would profit from an investigation into the 'physical conditions of the deep sea'.

Above: *The 1872–76 expedition by HMS* Challenger *was the first major voyage of discovery to scientifically investigate the oceans.*

CHALLENGER UNITES STRANDS OF OCEAN SCIENCE

Wyville Thomson and Carpenter's desired expedition came to fruition in December 1872, when HMS *Challenger* departed Portsmouth at the start of a three-and-a-half-year circumnavigation. It was the first major voyage of discovery with the specific aim of gathering scientific information about the oceans. In addition to studying seawater chemistry, material on the seabed and the distribution of living organisms, the expedition was directed to: 'Investigate the Physical Conditions of the Deep Sea, in the great Ocean basins – the North and South Atlantic, the North and South Pacific, and the Southern Ocean (as far as the neighbourhood of the great ice-barrier); in regard to Depth, Temperature, Circulation, Specific Gravity, and Penetration of Light; the observations and experiments upon all these points being made at various ranges of depth from the surface to the bottom.'

Challenger was a 61 m (200 ft), three-masted corvette, powered by both steam and sail. Fifteen of its 17 original guns were removed to make way for laboratories and to provide storage for dredging and sounding lines. On board the ship were 263 crew members commanded by Captain George S. Nares, and a team of five scientists led by Wyville Thomson. These 'Scientifics', as the crew referred to them, were: Canadian naturalist John Murray; British naturalist Henry Nottidge Moseley; German zoologist Rudolf von Willemoes Suhm; Scottish chemist John Young Buchanan; and Swiss artist and secretary to Wyville Thomson, John James Wild.

The ship headed first for Gibraltar and then out into the Atlantic, where the scientists began to undertake regular sounding and dredging operations. As Wyville Thomson wrote: 'We always kept in view that to explore the conditions of the deep sea was the primary object of our mission, and throughout the voyage we took every possible opportunity of making a deep-sea observation.'

Left: *HMS* Challenger *was well equipped to conduct sounding and dredging operations.*

The *Challenger* carried the men more than 68,000 nautical miles: south to Antarctica; to Australia and New Zealand; Fiji and the Philippines; New Guinea, Hong Kong, the Admiralty Islands and Tahiti; and down to the southern tip of South America, before returning home. Along the way, the scientists took measurements at 362 sampling stations, involving 492 depth soundings and 133 dredges. At each station the men sought to: record the exact depth; take the temperature of the seawater at the bottom, intermediate depths and the surface; gather a sample of the sea bottom from the sounding instrument; obtain a sample of seawater from the bottom and other depths for later chemical and physical analysis; dredge at the bottom, intermediate depths and the surface to collect samples of fauna; record the atmospheric and meteorological conditions; determine the rate and direction of currents at the surface; and, where pertinent, to ascertain the direction and rate of water movement at other depths.

This suite of measurements helped to build a more holistic understanding of the oceans. And the 4,700 new species the scientists dredged from various depths clearly demonstrated that life was present throughout the water column. But the expedition also made some other momentous discoveries, including the widespread presence of potato-sized manganese-rich nodules on the deep ocean floors (which mining companies today are keen to exploit) and the existence of a 'carbon compensation depth' (the depth at which carbonate dissolves at the same rate as it is supplied through the die-off of carbonate-rich surface plankton).

The finding that was to have the most impact on ocean understanding, however, was the discovery of the Mid-Atlantic Ridge, an underwater volcanic mountain range that snakes its way for 16,000 km (9,940 miles) from the Arctic to the Antarctic. A hundred years after its discovery, its

Opposite: *Maps produced from data gathered by the HMS* Challenger *expedition helped to reveal the ocean depths.*

Above: *The expedition discovered the existence of manganese-rich nodules in the deep ocean.*

presence would help to revolutionize geologic understanding of the world by supporting the theory of plate tectonics.

After the *Challenger* returned in 1876, its findings were meticulously written up, primarily by Murray, in 50 large volumes. These were published in 1895. The last two volumes comprised a summary of the results, in which Murray described the finished report as 'the greatest advance in the knowledge of our planet since the celebrated geographical discoveries of the fifteenth and sixteenth centuries.'

Today, the expedition's name lives on in the Challenger Deep, the point with the world's greatest known ocean depth, which lies within the 2,415 km (1,500 miles) long, crescent-shaped Mariana Trench. The *Challenger* scientists had been able to obtain a depth reading of 4,475 fathoms (8 km/5 miles) within the Trench. In 1951, HMS *Challenger II* accurately recorded the depth of the Challenger Deep as 5,940 fathoms (10.8 km/6.7 miles) using modern echo-sounding technology.

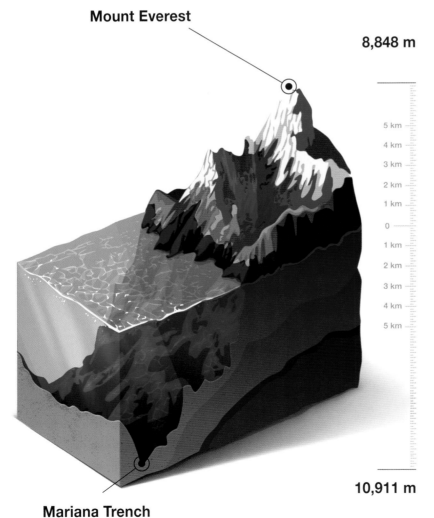

Mount Everest

8,848 m

5 km
4 km
3 km
2 km
1 km

0

1 km
2 km
3 km
4 km
5 km

10,911 m

Mariana Trench

Left: *The height of Mount Everest is less than the depth of the Mariana trench.*

Above: *A Chinese scientific expedition sets out to dive the Mariana Trench.*

Only four people have been to the bottom of the Challenger Deep; Jacques Piccard and Don Walsh took five hours to descend to the bottom in a US Navy submersible in 1960, and James Cameron descended in two hours and 26 minutes in 2012 on a solo dive in the *Deepsea Challenger* submersible in 2012. Victor Vescovo set the record for the deepest solo dive in history when he travelled to the depth of 10,927 metres (35,853 ft) in 2019.

CHAPTER 5
NEW TECHNOLOGIES UNDERPIN THE RISE OF OCEANOGRAPHY

Continuing technological advances aid exploration above and below the waves. Revelations from the sea floor help scientists to unravel the geological workings of the Earth. And the new field of oceanography develops, as diving suits and submersibles take scientists into the depths.

Left: RMS Titanic *was believed to be unsinkable when the ship hit an iceberg and sank in 1912.*

TITANIC SINKING PROMPTS SEARCH FOR TECHNOLOGY TO IMPROVE SAFETY AT SEA

The sinking of RMS *Titanic* following its collision with an iceberg on its maiden Atlantic voyage in 1912 was among the first major news stories to unfold on radio. Radio operators on shore were able to eavesdrop on messages from the rescue ship *Carpathia* and *Titanic*'s sister ship *Olympia*, and relayed what they heard to the newspapers. Word spread quickly of the loss of the 'unsinkable' ship together with more than 1,500 of *Titanic*'s estimated 2,208 passengers and crew.

One man who had been instrumental in advancing radio technology was the Canadian inventor Reginald Fessenden. Twelve years before the great ship's sinking, he had transmitted the first ever voice message between two towers one mile (1.6 km) apart at Brant Rock, Massachusetts. He had achieved this using amplitude modulation to enhance the strength of radio waves. After hearing of the *Titanic*'s demise by an unseen iceberg, 'Fessenden's mind grappled with the problem of divesting sea travel of this horror.'

Shortly after the disaster, Fessenden began working as a consultant for the Submarine Signal Company (SSC) in Boston, USA. The company manufactured underwater communications equipment, primarily aimed at sending audible warnings from shore to ships via bells on land and underwater microphones (hydrophones) on vessels. A problem, however, was that the hydrophones often picked up background noise that drowned out the sound of the warning bells. Fessenden's task was to develop a more effective hydrophone.

Fessenden, however, felt he could do better than that. Instead of focusing on the hydrophone, as requested, he developed the Fessenden oscillator, a more sophisticated piece of equipment that provided a superior sound source and was capable of both transmitting messages in Morse Code and receiving echoes that bounced back off surrounding surfaces. The kit proved its worth in underwater telegraphy when SSC engineers successfully transmitted messages between two tugboats several miles apart in Boston harbour in early 1913.

Right: *Reginald Fessenden invented an oscillator for underwater telegraphy, which was also capable of echo-sounding to calculate depths and distances to objects.*

Left: *The Hayes Sonic Depth Finder was used to produce the first bathymetric map.*

Below: *Operation of the Fathometer, which incorporated Fessenden's oscillator.*

A few months later, Fessenden tested his invention's echo-sounding capabilities from a Coast Guard cutter off the Grand Banks, southeast of Newfoundland. He successfully used the time taken for echoes to return from nearby underwater surfaces to calculate the distance to an iceberg and the depth of the seabed. During World War I, German, French and American technicians modified and enhanced the technology, employing it for both submarine detection and taking depth soundings.

In 1922, the Hayes Sonic Depth Finder, developed by American Harvey C. Hayes and incorporating the oscillator, was used onboard USS *Corry* and USS *Hull* to produce the first ever bathymetric map – of the California coast – based solely on echo-sounding (bathymetry is the measurement of water depth). Three years later, the German *Meteor* expedition, which was equipped with both an Atlas sounder (the depth-sounding Fathometer produced by SSC based on Fessenden's oscillator) and the German-developed Signal sounder, helped to cement the benefits of echo-sounding technology.

OPERATION OF THE FATHOMETER

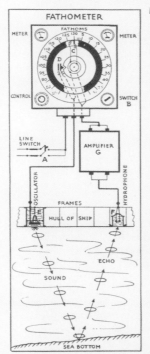

THE Fathometer Indicator, shown in this diagram, consists essentially of a disc mounted on the end of a shaft and driven by a small constant speed motor equipped with a governor. The motor is started by closing the Line Switch "A" and turning the Fathometer Switch "B". Mounted behind a radial slot in the disc is a Neon tube "C". In front of the disc is a circular scale which is graduated from 2 to 130 fathoms and lies just outside the path of the slot in front of the Neon tube.

Sound Production

A cam on the revolving shaft opens an electrical contact "D", thus allowing the Oscillator "E" to operate at the moment that the Neon tube is at the top of the scale. The Oscillator "E" produces a sound of short duration.

Sound Reception

The sound "echo" returning from the sea bottom is "picked up" by the Hydrophone "F" and a voltage is generated in the Hydrophone circuit. This voltage is transmitted through the Amplifier "G" causing a flash of light in the Neon tube "C" which, by this time, has traveled part way around the Fathometer dial. Acting like a luminous pointer, the flash of light indicates the depth at that instant. The disc to which the Neon tube is mounted makes several revolutions per minute and light flashes of the Neon tube, indicating depth, follow each other in rapid succession. If the bottom is level, the flashes will appear at the same point on the dial, but where the bottom is irregular it follows that they will vary in location in accordance with the contour of the bottom.

During the two-year expedition, the *Meteor* crisscrossed the Atlantic
14 times from the northern Tropics to Antarctica. The scientists on board,
led by German oceanographer Alfred Merz until his death early on in the
expedition, took 67,400 depth soundings at intervals of between 5 and 20
miles. They used the new technology to remeasure soundings taken on the
Challenger expedition and at the spot where the USS *Dolphin* had recorded
the deepest point in the Atlantic some 70 years earlier. Profiles of the Atlantic
floor generated from the depth data demonstrated for the first time that the
Mid-Atlantic Ridge was a rugged subsea mountain range.

Below: *The German* Meteor *expedition used the new echo-sounding technology to make 67,400 depth soundings across the Atlantic.*

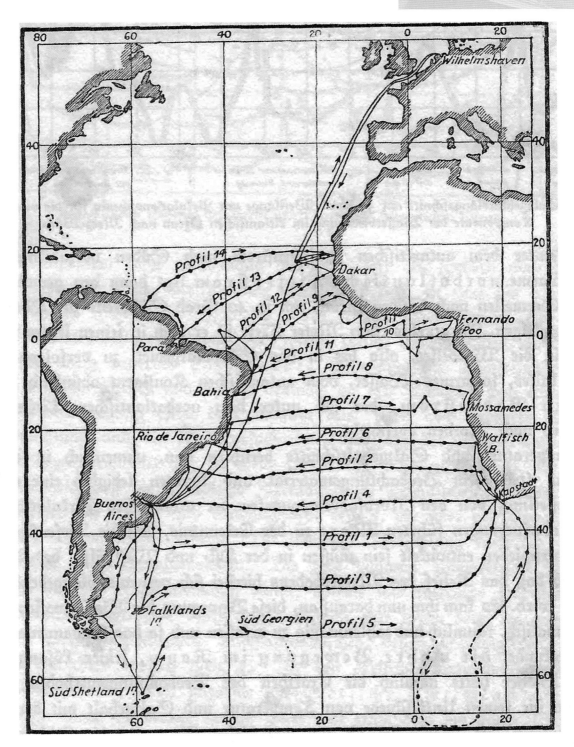

Right: *Tracks of the* Meteor *expedition across the Atlantic.*

Within 15 years of the *Titanic*'s sinking, the oscillator invented by Fessenden and further developed by other technicians had replaced the centuries-old line-sounding method for ascertaining ocean depths. Fessenden had paved the way for great strides to be made in ocean science in the years to come. He had also achieved his initial aim of making sea travel safer: as well as identifying objects in the water, mariners could now take accurate and frequent soundings, and compare them with a chart to find their course and position. In recognition of this and various other inventions, *Scientific American* awarded its Safety at Sea Gold Medal to Fessenden in 1929.

OCEAN-FLOOR STUDIES REVEAL GEOLOGICAL WORKINGS OF THE EARTH

It is much easier to map exposed land than ocean floors. So it is surprising that marine scientists, rather than terrestrial geologists, led the way in deciphering the global geological processes that shaped Earth in the past and remain operational today. Solving this scientific riddle did not happen overnight, however. It required careful detective work by many scientific minds over several decades, starting in the 1940s, and was only finally made possible by advances in gathering and interpreting large volumes of data.

The line where ocean meets land provided the first clue. The German meteorologist Alfred Wegener noted, as had others before him, that the coastlines of eastern South America and western Africa had a similar shape. He suggested this was because they had once been joined together. His 1912 theory of 'continental drift' proposed that, 250 million years ago, the modern-day continents had been part of a single landmass, Pangea. This had broken up, with the resulting new landmasses subsequently travelling, over millions of years, thousands of miles from their origin.

Wegener considered that forces within the Earth had driven continental blocks through weaker oceanic crust to rest in their current positions. His theory was accepted for several decades but then it fell out of favour. Geophysicists, who were by now using seismic waves and measurements of Earth's gravitational field to study the planet's interior, concluded that no natural forces existed with sufficient power to drive continents through oceanic crust. Nonetheless, the presence of similar fossils on either side of the Atlantic lent weight to the idea that the two landmasses had once been connected.

Below: *Diagram showing the movements of landmasses over time through continental drift.*

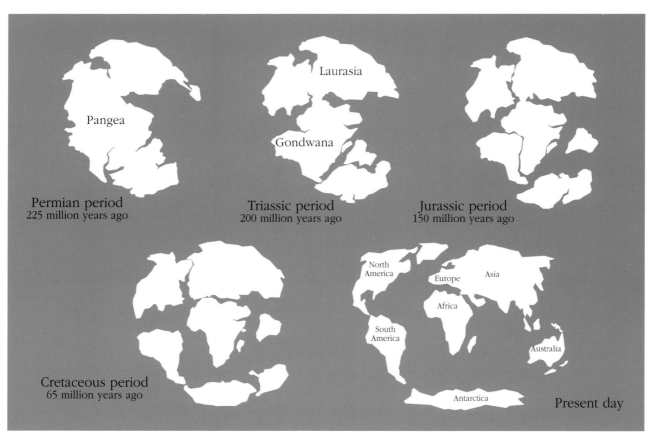

Pangea

Laurasia

Gondwana

Permian period
225 million years ago

Triassic period
200 million years ago

Jurassic period
150 million years ago

Cretaceous period
65 million years ago

North America

Europe

Asia

Africa

South America

Australia

Antarctica

Present day

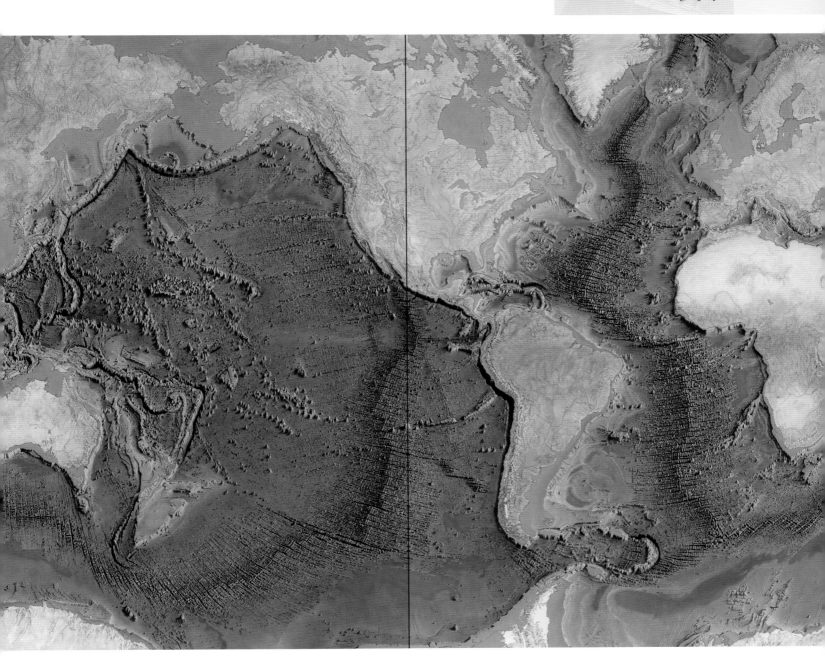

Above: *This world ocean floor map, produced in 1977 and based on the work of Marie Tharp and Bruce Heezen, clearly shows the Mid-Atlantic Ridge.*

Technology developed during World War II supported oceanic research that had not previously been possible. For example, the further development of echo-sounding and sonar facilitated the collection of great swathes of data that could be used to create profiles of the sea floor. Working at Columbia University's Lamont Geological Laboratory (now the Lamont-Doherty Earth Observatory) in the late 1940s and early 1950s, geologist Marie Tharp used such data to produce a map of the Atlantic floor. Her work, in collaboration with Bruce Heezen, confirmed the presence of an extensive mid-Atlantic mountain range with what appeared to be a valley-like cleft in the middle. The terrain resembled volcanic rift zones found on land. Subsequent work revealed that the ridge was 16,100 km (10,000 miles) long and that extensive trenches also existed on the seabed close to its boundaries with continental land.

Building on Tharp's and other studies, the American geophysicist Harry Hess developed a theory of 'sea floor spreading', which he published in 1960. In it, he suggested that molten rock continuously rose up to the Earth's surface at mid-ocean ridges, forming new sea floor. As this new material emerged at the ridge, older ocean floor would move away from it. Hess felt that this movement could explain the idea of continental drift; as the sea floor spread apart, so major landmasses were driven away. He proposed convection currents as the driver of the movement and suggested that the oldest sea floor was consumed in oceanic trenches at the boundaries with continents. Low gravity readings at trenches supported this theory. Another scientist, Robert Dietz, put forward a similar hypothesis.

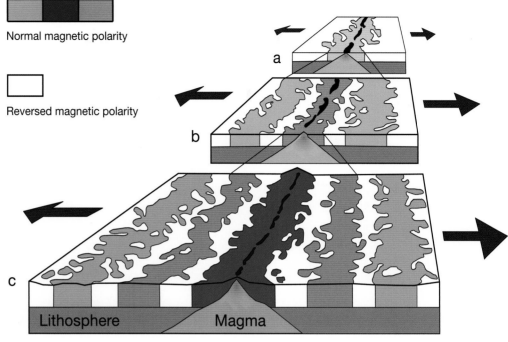

Normal magnetic polarity

Reversed magnetic polarity

Lithosphere   Magma

Above: *Seafloor spreading over time (oldest = farthest away; most recent = closest). The lithosphere comprises the crust and upper mantle.*

Work to understand magnetism had been conducted for centuries (see box on page 143 – Earth's magnetic characteristics slowly revealed). During World War II, magnetic airborne detectors carried on aeroplanes had been invaluable in detecting submarines. After the war, oceanographers began towing similar equipment behind research vessels to measure the strength of the Earth's magnetic field. When they measured magnetism on either side of mid-ocean ridges, they noted that running parallel to the ridge were linear patterns of alternating positively magnetized and negatively magnetized areas. In places, the ridges and stripes were offset by geological faults running perpendicular to them.

By the early 1960s, scientists understood that the polarity of Earth's magnetic field flipped back and forth between north and south at regular intervals. Soon a timescale of such events was developed, compiled from evidence recorded in rocks around the world. Once sufficient magnetic data had been gathered from the South Atlantic, Indian Ocean and South Pacific, the academics were able to conclude that the stripy pattern of magnetism on sea floors was evidence of magnetic reversals that had happened over long periods of time as new oceanic crust formed at mid-ocean ridges and older sea floor moved away from them. Evidence of magnetic reversals observed in deep-sea cores proved the theory of sea floor spreading beyond doubt.

Left: *Calibrating magnetic detectors on a ship.*

At around the same time, the Canadian geophysicist John Tuzo-Wilson proposed a theory to explain how volcanic island chains such as Hawaii were formed – by the movement of oceanic crust over a hotspot in the Earth's mantle (the molten part of the Earth between the solid crust and its denser, iron-nickel core). He hypothesized that Earth's crust was divided into rigid plates, predicting that plates were pulled apart at mid-ocean ridges, pushed together where ocean trenches and terrestrial mountain ranges occurred, and slid past each other in locations featuring large faults – which he named 'transform faults'. He considered that a 'triple junction' occurred at the boundary between three plates.

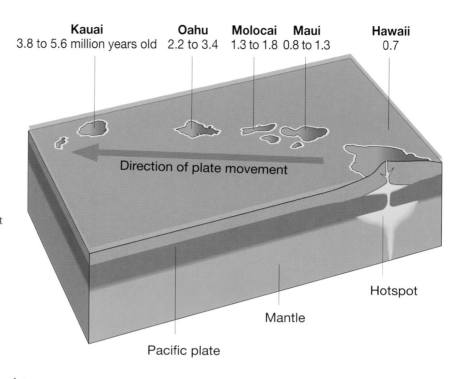

Kauai
3.8 to 5.6 million years old

Oahu
2.2 to 3.4

Molocai
1.3 to 1.8

Maui
0.8 to 1.3

Hawaii
0.7

Direction of plate movement

Hotspot

Mantle

Pacific plate

In 1964, Lamont seismologists Bryan Isacks and Jack Oliver began to investigate deep earthquakes occurring around Fiji and Tonga. Both were locations known to have the greatest number of deep earthquakes in the world. By plotting where the earthquakes occurred, they deduced that the quakes were being caused by a slab of oceanic crust being forced or pulled down into the mantle. This was evidence that ocean floor being created at mid-ocean ridges was compensated for by the consumption of older oceanic crust in 'subduction zones', at the boundaries between oceans and land.

Above: *The Hawaiian islands formed in sequence, as the Pacific Plate moved over a 'hotspot' in the mantle.*

Left: *The volcanic island chain that forms the Hawaiian islands, as seen from space.*

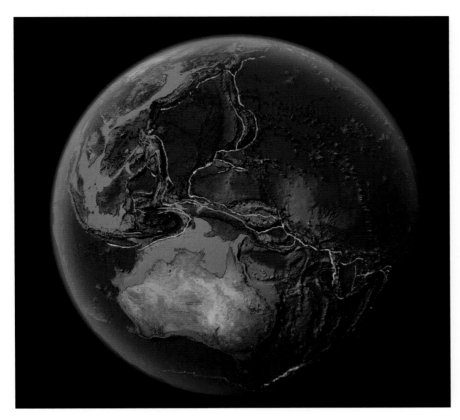

Mathematical modelling using computers confirmed that the proposed movements of plates followed geometrical principles and tallied with seismic data from subduction zones. In 1968, Isacks, Oliver and fellow seismologist Lynn R. Sykes synthesized the findings of Wegener, Hess, Dietz, Wilson and others in the paper *Seismology and the New Global Tectonics*. From the deepest ocean trench to the tallest mountains on land, the theory – now known as plate tectonics – provided a framework for explaining Earth's geological features past and present.

Left: *Seven major tectonic plates make up the Earth's crust. This satellite-based globe shows plate boundaries in the western Pacific Ocean.*

Earth's magnetic characteristics slowly revealed

As early as 1269, the French scholar Peter Peregrinus studied the magnetic characteristics of lodestones (naturally magnetized pieces of the mineral magnetite). He concluded that they had two ends, or 'poles', capable of attracting or repelling other lodestones; that floating lodestones tended to align themselves north–south; and that lodestone could magnetize an iron needle. This last property was put to use with the invention of the compass. Sailors who used early compasses realized that their needles did not point to true geographic north but to a magnetic pole offset from true north.

The English physician William Gilbert concluded around 1600 that the Earth itself was magnetized and that lodestone magnetism was related to this. Investigations in the seventeenth century revealed that once-molten rocks preserved a record of the Earth's magnetic field at the time of their cooling. Subsequent studies of geological formations around the world revealed that the Earth's magnetic pole had switched back and forth between north and south many times in the past.

Above: *William Gilbert demonstrating magnetism to Queen Elizabeth I of England.*

Building up a picture of the ocean floor

In the early eighteenth century, the Italian naturalist and geographer Count Luigi Ferdinando
Marsili hitched rides with coral fishermen in the Gulf of Lyons, off France's Mediterranean
coast, and, drawing on routine navigation practice, took depth soundings using a simple lead
and line. On drawing profiles of the seabed, he found the sea was relatively shallow close to
the coast but then dropped away to greater depths. In his book *Histoire Physique de la Mer*
(1725), he predicted that such a 'continental shelf' would also exist off the north African coast.

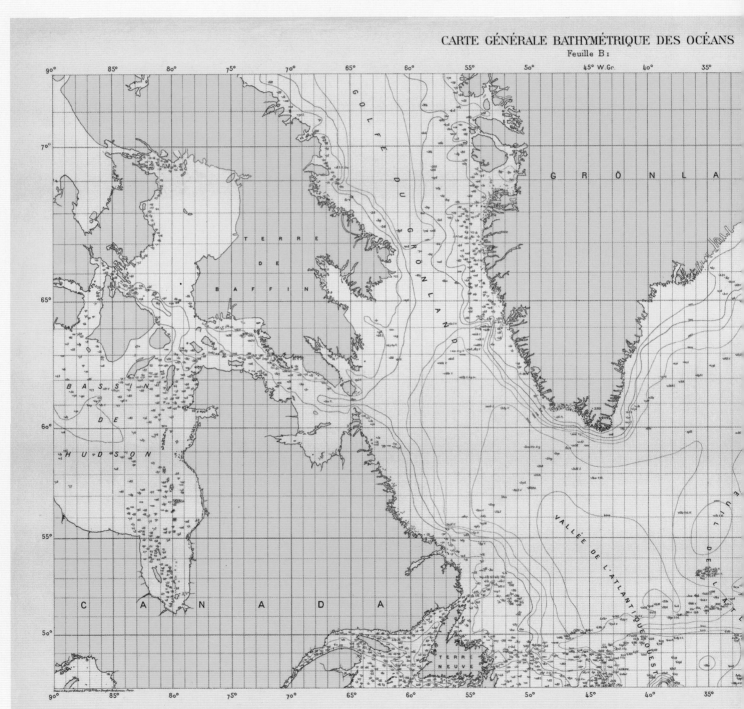

In 1903, ocean depth information collected by cable-laying ships, scientific cruises and polar expeditions, and published by the British and French Hydrographic Offices, was collated to form the first ever General Bathymetric Chart of the Oceans. The venture was supported by Prince Albert I of Monaco, who himself had studied oceanography and conducted many ocean expeditions. Showing the contours of the seabed and setting a standard nomenclature for describing ocean floors, the map clearly highlighted the presence of continental shelves worldwide. A second edition of the map published between 1910 and 1931 included land contours at the same interval as those included for sea areas.

As echo-sounding yielded increasing volumes of data, scientists became aware that the edges of continental shelves were incised by deep canyons. In 1936, the Canadian-American geologist Reginald Daly hypothesized that dense, sediment-rich currents carved these canyons when they flowed downhill under the force of gravity. In the early 1950s, American geologists at Lamont Geological Observatory were able to prove this when they examined records from a major earthquake that had struck Grand Banks, south of Newfoundland in 1929.

The data showed that a series of subsea telegraph cables, some of them located 480 km (300 miles) from the earthquake epicentre, had broken sometime after the quake. Around a dozen cables appeared to have snapped, one after the other, from the top of the continental shelf to the bottom. The scientists realized that the earthquake had triggered an underwater avalanche, or 'turbidity current', which had snapped the cables in sequence as it sped down the continental slope at some 72 km/h (45 mph).

We now know that such currents involve movement of the seafloor as well as sediment-laden seawater. They shift huge volumes of sediments into the deep ocean and are important in the formation of oil reserves.

Left: *The first General Bathymetric Chart of the Oceans was introduced in 1903. Revisions have been made regularly ever since.*

Below: *An underwater avalanche or 'turbidity current'.*

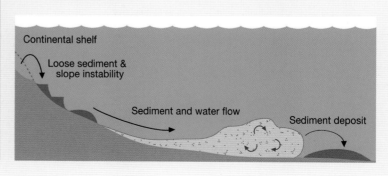

Continental shelf

Loose sediment & slope instability

Sediment and water flow

Sediment deposit

TECHNOLOGY TAKES OCEANOGRAPHY BENEATH THE WAVES

Our quest to explore the ocean depths

From the ancient Egyptians' and Greeks' first experiments with diving (see Chapter 1, page 37), humans continued to seek ways to survive under water. During the Renaissance, inventors had some success with diving bells that trapped air beneath a container as it was submerged. One such bell enabled items to be salvaged, in 1531, from a Roman galley that had sunk in Italy's Lake Nemi. In 1687, William Phips, of the Massachusetts Bay Colony in North America, used a diving bell to recover a significant amount of treasure from a Spanish galleon in the West Indies.

Below: *The remains of a Roman ship recovered from Lake Nemi in 1929. Divers had recovered items from the site as far back as the 16th century.*

Right: *Physicist Robert Boyle realized that increasing the pressure exerted on a gas-filled object, such as a balloon, shrinks its volume in a predictable way.*

Improvements in our understanding of how gases behave under pressure helped to drive the development of more sophisticated diving bells during the late seventeenth century. The Anglo-Irish physicist Robert Boyle realized, for example, that increasing the pressure exerted on a gas-filled object, such as a balloon, will shrink its volume in a predictable way. This led the French priest Abbé Jean de Hautefeuille to conclude that: 'It is not possible for man to breathe air at normal atmospheric pressure when he is himself under water at depth.' The English inventor John Lethbridge and astronomer Sir Edmund Halley both created sophisticated diving machines taking into account Boyle's Law. A refined version of Halley's bell was commonly used in harbours for repair, salvage and construction operations by the start of the nineteenth century.

Right: *A diving bell created by astronomer Edmund Halley, taking into account Boyle's law.*

Innovations during the next 100 years paved the way for the development of modern diving systems. One was Deane's Patent Diving Apparatus, comprising a helmet supplied with air and separate suit with weighted shoes. Some sources report that the inspiration for this came from John Deane's quick thinking during a fire in Whitstable, UK, in 1820. When firefighters were held back by thick smoke, Deane suggested they pump air into the helmet from a suit of armour that was on display nearby. The story goes that, wearing this, he was able to breathe sufficiently well to rescue a team of horses from the flames. The diving dress was later refined by the German Augustus Siebe, who joined the helmet to the suit and improved the apparatus's exhaust system. Later adopted as standard for the British Royal Engineers, the Siebe Improved Diving Dress was a precursor to modern-day military diving suits.

Above: *Divers use Augustus Siebe's diving dress to salvage the guns from the HMS* Royal George *in the 1840s.*

Functional self-contained diving suits also emerged during the nineteenth century. Among early designs was the Aerophore, which featured an air reservoir carried on the back and a regulator that controlled the delivery of air. Although designed primarily to be supplied with air from the surface, it was also able to function independently. The Aerophore was the inspiration for the diving suits described by Jules Verne in his 1870 novel *Twenty-Thousand Leagues Under the Sea.*

Right: *The Aerophore inspired Jules Verne's descriptions of diving suits in his novel* Twenty Thousand Leagues under the Sea.

Above: *Paul Bert contributed to knowledge on decompression sickness.*

A downside of such self-contained diving systems was that their requirement for large air reservoirs made them somewhat inefficient. This led inventors to investigate alternative methods of supplying air, including oxygen rebreathers (which processed carbon dioxide and recirculated unused oxygen) and high-pressure tanks (which could hold greater volumes of air). Research by Frenchman Paul Bert and Scotsman John Scott Haldane complemented technological advances by helping to explain decompression sickness and to outline the safe limits for diving with compressed air.

By the 1930s, the first automatic Self-Contained Underwater Breathing Apparatus (SCUBA) had been developed by Frenchman George Commeinhes, including a full-face mask, compressed air tanks and a demand-valve-controlled air supply. In the 1940s, Jacques-Yves Cousteau and Émile Gagnan developed a similar set-up but did away with the full-face mask. In their model, air was supplied through a separate mouthpiece in response to the diver's intake of breath. The equipment was successfully tested to a depth of 67 m (220 ft) in 1943 and patented as the Aqua Lung. The subsequent evolution of SCUBA through technological advances, and the creation of organized diving training programmes, elevated diving from a niche activity undertaken by a few enthusiasts to a recreational sport that has allowed millions of people around the world to explore the underwater environment (see box on page 154 – Recreational diving takes marine scientists into the shallows).

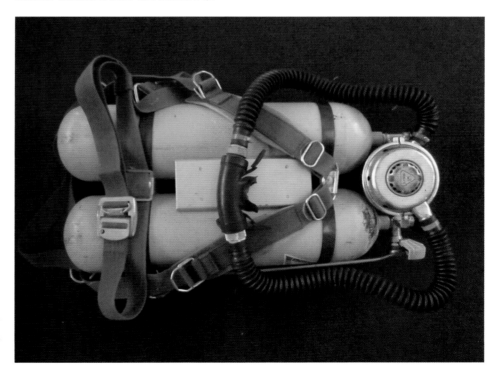

Right: *The Aqua Lung developed by Jacques-Yves Costeau and Emile Gagnan.*

The 1930s, too, saw the launch of the submersible known as the bathysphere (from the Greek *bathus* meaning deep). By then, submarines were well established for military use, but this was the first time a vessel had been developed specifically for studying the undersea environment and wildlife. Created by naturalist and ornithologist William Beebe and engineer Otis Barton, the submersible was a sphere with a diameter of 1.45m (4 ft 9 in) and made of thick, cast-iron walls to withstand the great pressures at depth. Oxygen tanks with automatic valves provided the cramped inhabitants with air, while chemicals absorbed exhaled carbon dioxide and moisture. The vessel was winched into the sea from a ship using a non-twisting steel cable 1,100 m (3,500 ft) long. Electricity and a telephone line were supplied through a rubber hose, via a stuffing box to prevent the ingress of water, into the top of the bathysphere.

Above: *Naturalist William Beebe (left) and engineer Otis Barton with their bathysphere.*

Beebe and Barton conducted numerous dives in the early years of the 1930s. The deepest dive, in 1934, took them to a record-breaking 925 m (3,028 ft). These dives provided the first opportunity for observing deep-sea creatures in their natural habitat. Many animals they observed, including some bioluminescent ones that glowed in the dark, had never been seen before. On each dive, Beebe described by telephone the creatures he saw to scientists at the top who recorded his observations. In Beebe's 1934 book *Half Mile Down* he concluded that 'a much more abundant and larger-sized fish fauna exists in these waters than is in any way adumbrated by six years of trawling with the best possible oceanographic collecting outfit.'

When Beebe invited ichthyologist John Tee-Van to accompany him on a dive to 455 m (1,500 ft), the scientist was greatly surprised at the variety of sea animals living at depth:

> *Thirty minutes at the greatest depth left me exhausted with excitement, full of too many things seen and incapable of absorbing more; fish succeeded fish, and shrimps followed shrimps. A siphonophore four inches long with delicate upper bract and trailing tentacle passed the window. Two or three leptocephalids came into sight, one of them about eight inches in length, elongate and narrow and probably of the common type. As we approached the surface, larger organisms became fewer, while the abundance of minute life in the sea again manifested itself; outside our window were the myriad motes of creatures that scintillated in the dilute yellow sunlight.*

Barton and Beebe's deep-sea exploits inspired Auguste Piccard to develop a more advanced deep-sea submersible, called a bathyscaphe. Piccard was an inventor and physicist who, in 1931, had built a balloon with pressurized cabin that carried him to an altitude of 15,780 m (51,775 ft). He was equally interested in travelling to the depths of the oceans, and he used his knowledge of building balloons to design a new kind of craft for undertaking deep dives. Specifically, he incorporated

a balloon-like float filled with gasoline to help buoyancy: this low-density liquid is relatively incompressible and so will remain buoyant even as pressure increases. In order to descend, the vessel dumped gas (since gas is lighter than water) or took on seawater. And shedding ballast at the end of a dive prompted its return to the surface. This freed the bathyscaphe from needing to be lowered on a line from a support ship.

Left: *Auguste Piccard, who developed the bathyscaphe submersible.*

Above: *Piccard's* Trieste *bathyscaphe.*

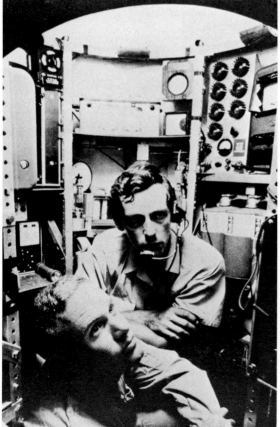

Left: *Inside the* Trieste *bathyscaphe.*

In 1953, two incarnations of this vessel engaged in a race to the bottom: Piccard's *Trieste* (named after the home town of funder Professor Diego de Henriquez) achieved a dive of 3,167 m (10,390 ft) while *FNRS-3* (named after the initial Belgian funder the *Fonds National de la Recherche Scientifique* and subsequently purchased by the French Navy) achieved a dive of 4,100 m (13,450 ft). In 1958, the US Navy acquired *Trieste* and replaced its cabin in preparation for even deeper dives. It was in this version of the bathyscaphe that Auguste's son, Jacques Piccard, and Don Walsh achieved their record-breaking journey of 10,916 m (35,814 ft) to the Challenger Deep in 1960 (see page 131). As the *Trieste* reached the bottom, Piccard spotted a sole-like flatfish; life, it seemed, existed even in the deepest parts of the world's oceans.

Recreational diving takes marine scientists into the shallows

The development of the diving industry has brought great benefits to oceanography by enabling scientists to observe ocean shallows in real time and to monitor change over periods of time at relatively low cost. It has made it much easier to gather information on the behaviour of marine organisms, to conduct geological and archaeological analyses, and to monitor the effects of climate change on submarine ecosystems. It has also enabled scientists to confirm conditions indicated in broader-scale observations made from aerial or satellite images, contributing to more accurate mapping.

Today, the growing interest in marine issues in society is helping to drive development of marine citizen science, where sport divers contribute data to scientific programmes. A study published in 2016 in *Nature*'s online journal *Scientific Reports* showed that temperature profiles captured by divers' wrist computers can augment existing monitoring systems by filling in knowledge gaps in poorly sampled or highly changeable coastal environments. The project – the first of its kind – collected more than 7,000 temperature records from recreational divers to construct a record of global sea temperature.

Left: *The recreational diving industry has provided a low-cost way for scientists to monitor shallow oceans.*

Disaster prompts advances in deep-sea submersibles

A military tragedy in 1963 highlighted a potential wider role for deep submersibles. While on a test dive, the US nuclear submarine USS *Thresher* malfunctioned and then imploded, with the loss of 129 personnel. As the US Navy had been planning to build a new class of submarines based on the *Thresher*, it needed to locate the wreck and find out what had gone wrong. The Navy despatched its recently acquired *Trieste* bathyscaphe to search an area of around 260 square kilometres (100 square miles) for the wreck. This was no easy task, given the vessel's slow pace and the difficulties of tracking its position. However, on the third dive, an on-board operator spotted the remains of *Thresher* 2.4 km (1.5 miles) down off the coast of New England.

Below: *The launch of the US nuclear submarine USS* Thresher, *which later imploded on a test dive.*

Mindful that a similar accident could happen in future, the Navy formed the Deep Submergence Systems Project, which stimulated action to research and develop new submersibles. At the time, the US economy was strong, and military engineers were already engaged in building state-of-the-art aircraft, submarines and spaceships. The development of deep-sea technology for salvage operations seemed a natural add-on. Within a year, a new, more nimble, deep-sea submersible had been launched by the Office for Naval Research and the Woods Hole Oceanographic Institution (the latter established in 1930 to conduct research into marine sciences and engineering). It was named *Alvin* in honour of Allyn Vine, a Woods Hole oceanographer and champion of crewed deep-sea exploration.

Relatively lightweight at 17 tons (17 long tons), *Alvin* had a 6.7 m (2 ft) long white fibreglass hull containing a thick-walled steel pressure sphere. It was made buoyant with syntactic foam (fashioned from preformed hollow spheres). The vessel was capable of going to a depth of 1,830 m (6,000 ft). In 1966, when a hydrogen bomb was lost in the Mediterranean Sea following a collision by an Air Force B-52 bomber and a tanker over Spain, *Alvin* got its first major deployment. The bomb was successfully recovered, underpinning confidence in the submersible's capacity to operate on the sea floor.

Below: *The deep-sea submersible Alvin, launched in 1965 by the Office for Naval Research and the Woods Hole Oceanographic Institution.*

Right: *Inside the* Ben Franklin *mesoscaphe, which could house six scientists for several weeks.*

By the early 1970s, plans were afoot to use *Alvin* on Project FAMOUS (French-American Mid-Ocean Undersea Study). This ambitious scientific programme aimed to dive to the Mid-Atlantic Ridge between 36° and 37° North. The hope was that scientists would for the first time be able to inspect the boundary of a crustal plate, where new crust was being formed by sea floor spreading. In preparation, *Alvin*'s steel personnel sphere was replaced with a titanium one, enabling it to dive to 3,660 m (12,000 ft).

During the course of 42 dives, made on 25 separate cruises to the target area, the scientists encountered new volcanic forms, large cracks and fissures in the seabed, and metallic deposits that appeared to have been laid down by hot-water streams. They took 100,000 photographs of the seabed, gathered rock, sediment and water samples from precisely recorded locations, and extracted two cores. Their work helped to show that the sea floor was not being pushed, but rather was being pulled apart – a previously contested topic. *Alvin* had performed exceptionally well and, in the words of James Heirtzler of Woods Hole, who headed up the US team on the project, made it 'relatively easy for scientists to work at the bottom of a deep ocean'.

Other submersibles were by now in operation, too, their development prompted both by the Navy's call for research into marine technologies, and speculation about the potential oil and mineral resources that might lie in the deep. Among these new craft was the *Ben Franklin*, a mesoscaphe or middle-depth submersible, designed by Jacques Piccard. Capable of housing six people for 30 days, the vessel was designed to explore the Gulf Stream – first mapped by Benjamin Franklin all those years ago – by drifting with the current at a depth of 150–550 m (500–1,800 ft) for 2,410 km (1,500 miles). The mesoscaphe was equipped with state-of-the-art equipment, enabling it to measure gravity, the Earth's magnetic field, the amount of light absorbed by the water, current speeds and direction, temperature, salinity, depth, water turbulence and sound velocity. It also carried side-scan sonar, technology evolved from early echo-sounders, enabling the scientists to accurately map the ocean floor.

Above: *Scientists on the* Ben Franklin *made more than two million scientific measurements while drifting in the Gulf Stream in 1969.*

Trackable from the surface, the vessel successfully drifted at around 4 km/h (2.5 mph) from off of the coast of Palm Beach, Florida to Halifax, Nova Scotia. Despite on-board conditions ranging from wintery to sauna-like, and the craft undergoing some dramatic fluctuations in depth, the expedition was a success. Altogether the crew made more than two million scientific measurements, which contributed to an understanding not only of oceanography and marine biology but also of how people work within challenging environments. With the expedition taking place in July 1969, its success was largely eclipsed by the Apollo 11 moon landing. However, data collected from it became the foundation of current knowledge about the Gulf Stream. It was now obvious that studying the oceans from within was not only possible but yielded far superior results than simply taking measurements from the surface.

The rise of oceanography

The field of oceanography emerged in the nineteenth century, as expeditions took to the seas to explore the biological, chemical and physical characteristics of the oceans. In particular, the *Challenger* expedition of 1872–76 helped to link studies into aspects such as marine life, water chemistry and the shape of the ocean floor. In the early twentieth century, Harald Sverdrup, Martin W. Johnson and Richard H. Fleming of the Scripps Institution of Oceanography, San Diego, USA, published *The Oceans: Their Physics, Chemistry and General Biology*. This helped to define oceanography as a unified discipline and also provided a framework for teaching the subject going forward. Technologies used during World War II drove advances in oceanographic knowledge, prompting an expansion of the subject. Today, oceanography continues to evolve, thanks to technological advances facilitating access to previously inhospitable places and increasing data-processing power.

Below: *Harald Sverdrup helped to define the field of oceanography.*

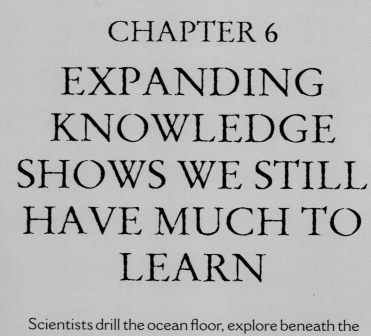

CHAPTER 6
EXPANDING KNOWLEDGE SHOWS WE STILL HAVE MUCH TO LEARN

Scientists drill the ocean floor, explore beneath the waves and observe the oceans from space. Their work yields a new theory for the beginnings of life and enhances our knowledge of marine species. However, it also provides evidence for climate change, and reveals how human activities have harmed marine environments. Gathering more data on the world's oceans is key to our future sustainable use of them.

Left: *The* JOIDES Resolution, *one of several ships used since the 1960s to extract cores from the ocean floor.*

DRILLING BENEATH THE SEA
REVEALS A WEALTH OF INFORMATION

During the 1930s, scientists experimented with using piston-coring methods to extract sections of sediment from the sea floor. This involved plunging a heavy tube into the sea bed to extract samples. Although coring was already in use by the oil industry by this time, the technology used was a closely guarded secret. Initially, the ocean scientists' efforts brought up cores of just a few metres but, by the time the Swedish *Albatross* expedition set sail in 1947, technology had advanced sufficiently for those on board to recover cores 15 m (49 feet) long. For the first time, researchers had direct access to a global repository of undisturbed sediments and rocks recording millions of years of ocean and climate history.

A chance for coring to progress as an investigative geological tool came in the early 1960s, with the launch of Project Mohole. Attempting to drill through the Mohorovičić discontinuity – the boundary between Earth's crust and mantle – a team of scientists attached four large outboard motors to the barge that served as a drilling platform, allowing it to be dynamically positioned. This enabled the team to keep the coring equipment steady and successfully drill through 170 m (558 ft) of sediments and 13 m (43 ft) of underlying basalt. The existence of basalt – a once molten igneous rock – helped to support the theory

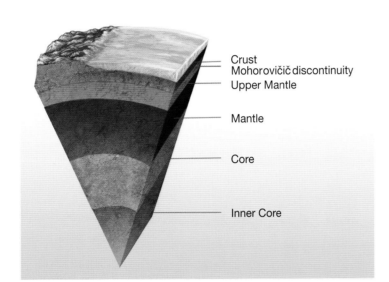

Crust
Mohorovičić discontinuity
Upper Mantle

Mantle

Core

Inner Core

Left: *The Mohorovičić discontinuity marks the boundary between the earth's crust and mantle.*

Below: *Project Mohole pioneered a new way to keep a ship in position while extracting long cores from the seabed.*

of continental drift. Although the initial plan foundered, the scientists earned a congratulatory telegram from US President John F. Kennedy for their achievement.

From 1966, a new phase of ocean drilling began with the Deep Sea Drilling Project. Running until 1983, this programme undertook drilling and coring in the Atlantic, Pacific and Indian Oceans, together with the Mediterranean and Red Seas. Employing the *Glomar Challenger* vessel (a name that honoured the ship's owner Global Marine Inc. and the famed oceanographic vessel HMS *Challenger*), it was a joint initiative by five US oceanographic institutions: Lamont Geological Observatory; the Institute of Marine and Atmospheric Sciences at the University of Miami; Scripps Institution of Oceanography; the University of Washington; and Woods Hole Oceanographic Institution.

Potentially the greatest achievement of the project was to prove the hypothesis of sea floor spreading, helping to underpin the theory of plate tectonics. Cores extracted from across the South Atlantic between America and Africa in 1968 confirmed that the age of the crust increased almost linearly with distance from the Mid-Atlantic Ridge. It also revealed ocean floors to be much younger than the oldest terrestrial geology; no more than 200 million years old, in comparison to the age of the Earth – 4.5 billion years. In 1975, Germany, Japan, the UK, the Soviet Union and France joined

Above: *Drilling undertaken from the* Glomar Challenger *helped to prove the hypothesis of seafloor spreading.*

forces with the USA to continue the work, heralding a period of exemplary international scientific collaboration.

When the project came to an end in 1983, it was replaced by the Ocean Drilling Program. Texas A&M University was Science Operator, and leased it a more modern and capable vessel. The ship was rechristened *JOIDES Resolution* (JOIDES standing for the Joint Oceanographic Institutions for Deep Earth Sampling). This facilitated a further 20 years of deep-sea drilling and coring by a wide number of international collaborators. A total of 222,430 m (729,757 ft) of core was recovered from 1,797 drill holes in ocean basins around the world. Scientific analysis of these samples helped to enhance understanding of plate tectonic processes; the make-up and structure of the Earth's crust; the environmental conditions that prevailed in ancient oceans; and climate change.

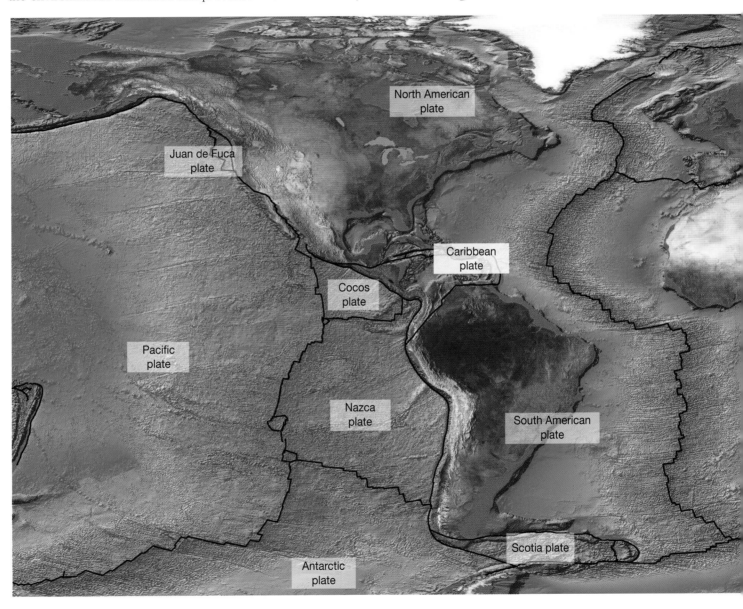

Above: *This image shows the age of the oceanic lithosphere. It is clear that the new seafloor (red) is created at mid-oceanic ridges.*

The programme did not formally end until 2003, but by the mid-1990s momentum was already building for a new ocean-drilling initiative to replace it. This came to fruition in 2003 as the Integrated Ocean Drilling Program (IODP), which employed several drilling platforms to enable scientists to reach new areas of the subsea surface. These were the refurbished *JOIDES Resolution*, the Japanese Deep Sea Drilling Vessel *Chikyu*, and various mission-specific platforms. After ten years, the IODP partners, drawn from 26 nations, continued operations as the International Ocean Discovery Program: Exploring the Earth Under the Sea.

The programme continues to this day, and cores extracted by it have helped show that Antarctica was once covered in tropical forests; revealed a 10-million-year record of sea-level fluctuations; shed light on the mechanics of underwater earthquakes; and yielded evidence of life in the deepest layer

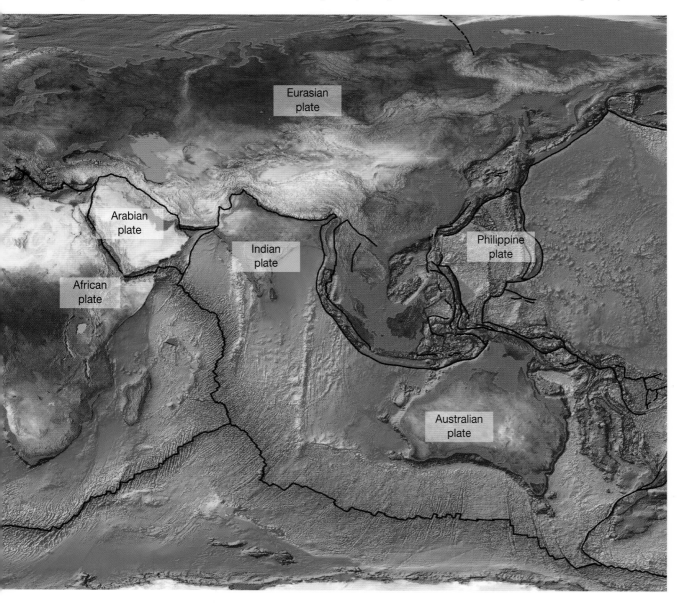

Age of oceanic lithosphere (million years)

0   20   40   60   80   100   120   140   160   180   200   220   240   260   280

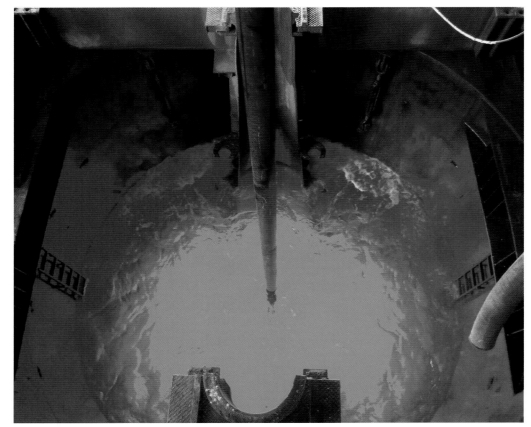

Left: *Drilling the deepest ocean core.*

of the Earth's crust, more than 1 km (0.6 miles) beneath the surface. The deepest ocean core drilled to date, at 1,927 m (6,322 ft), was extracted off of the coast of New Zealand in 2010. In December 1969, when ocean drilling was a new tool for oceanographers, Melvin N. A. Peterson of Scripps Institution of Oceanography had written in *Science*: 'It is difficult to imagine another project of national scope that might produce such profound results for so many branches of science.' His forecast for the value of ocean drilling has turned out to be uncannily accurate; over five decades it has revealed much about Earth's dynamic systems, from the history of Earth's climate to how ocean basins form. Writing in 2018, in a special issue of *Oceanography* celebrating 50 years of ocean drilling, Anthony A. P. Koppers and others concluded that: 'Scientific ocean drilling has matured in parallel with emerging challenges in the Earth, ocean, and life sciences, remaining as relevant a scientific endeavor as it was in the early days of the Deep Sea Drilling Project in the late 1960s.'

Right: *Scientists first witnessed seafloor spreading close to the Galápagos Islands, seen here.*

UNDERWATER DISCOVERY PROMPTS RETHINK ABOUT LIFE ON EARTH

During the early 1970s, oceanographers working close to the Galápagos Islands had detected earthquakes, recorded warmer-than-usual sea temperatures and spotted some unusual large white clams on an area of mid-ocean ridge. In 1977, an expedition set off to investigate the area more closely, using the deep-sea submersible *Alvin*. What the team of 30 marine geologists, geochemists and geophysicists discovered would offer a visual demonstration of sea floor spreading, disprove the hypothesis that life processes always take place slowly in the deep ocean, and lead to an entirely new hypothesis for the origins of life on Earth.

When the team arrived at the location of interest on the Galápagos Rift, they first dispatched the unmanned vessel ANGUS (Acoustically Navigated Geophysical Underwater System) to photograph the ocean floor. The resulting images revealed 'pillow' lavas, formed when magma emerging from cracks in the sea floor is cooled on contact with cold seawater; smooth, billowy lavas, similar to the *pahoehoe* type seen on Hawaii; and – in the place where the temperature anomalies had previously been recorded – a cloud of misty, blue water and hundreds of white clams and brown mussel shells. This was the first ever recording of a hydrothermal vent.

Left: *A type of hydrothermal vent known as a black smoker.*

When three scientists took *Alvin* down to the spot for a closer look, they found themselves in another world. Warm, shimmering water that poured from cracks in the lava quickly turned cloudy blue as chemicals precipitated out of it and were deposited on the lava surface. White clams, up to 30 cm (12 in) across, were concentrated around the outpourings. Visits to other vents located soon after this initial dive revealed other life, including limpets, white crabs and giant, white-stalked tube worms with red tops. At the time, creatures were thought to thrive in the deep sea only where sufficient food rained down from the surface. The researchers were mystified as to what these creatures could be living off in the pitch-blackness, at depths of more than 2,500 m (8,200 ft).

Right: *Pillow lava forms where molten rock is cooled quickly by seawater.*

What the scientists had witnessed was sea floor spreading in action and an entirely new kind of ecosystem. We now know that, in such locations on mid-ocean ridges, subsea magma chambers heat up the overlying rocks. Cold seawater that percolates down through cracks and comes into contact with these rocks is heated to high temperatures and begins to absorb minerals and chemicals. It erupts as a geyser through hydrothermal vents, with the chemicals that precipitate out on contact with the cold seawater forming chimneys around vents. The hot mineral-rich fluid provides a food source for microbes, which are either eaten by, or live symbiotically inside, deep-sea creatures. Giant tube worms of the genus *Riftia*, for example, provide a home for bacteria in exchange for food.

Above: Riftia *tube worms thrive close to hydrothermal vents.*

In most ecosystems on Earth, sunlight provides the energy source required to produce food. Organisms use solar energy to turn carbon dioxide and water into sugar and oxygen in a process called photosynthesis. All plants, and some bacteria, use this method of food production. Chemosynthetic organisms, by contrast, use the energy released by inorganic chemical reactions to generate food. Different species take various routes, but those living around hydrothermal vents primarily oxidize hydrogen sulfide, then add carbon dioxide and oxygen to produce sugar, sulphur and water. Between them, photosynthesis and chemosynthesis underpin all life on Earth.

Since the first few hydrothermal vents were explored in the 1970s, hundreds more have been found all over the world, hosting some 800 animal and numerous microbial species. They occur where magma comes into contact with seawater, at spreading ridges and convergent plate boundaries. Types include black smokers (where iron sulfide is deposited) and white smokers (where barium, calcium or silicon precipitate from the heated water).

Above: *Hydrothermal vents have now been found all over the world.*

The deepest known hydrothermal vent, a black smoker teeming with microbial mats, spiny anemones and shrimps, lies around 5,000 m (16,400 ft) down in the Caribbean Sea. And the hottest water, at 464°C (867°F), was recorded in two black smokers in the Atlantic Ocean in 2006 and 2007. This was the first time that water had been observed in nature occurring in a 'supercritical' state; being denser than vapour but much less dense than liquid water. Scientists have also found cold seeps, where water containing hydrocarbon-rich chemicals from petroleum deposits emerges from fissures created by plate tectonic movements.

Analyzing the chemicals added to and removed from seawater at hydrothermal vents and cold seeps is helping scientists to understand more about the processes that have kept seawater chemistry constant for millions of years. It is thought that the entire volume of the world's oceans passes through the global mid-ocean ridge system every 10–20 million years.

In recent years, support has grown for the theory that hydrothermal vents hosted the beginnings of life on Earth. A 2016 study led by the University of Dusseldorf, Germany, found that the last universal common ancestor (LUCA) emerged around 3.8 billion years ago. The researchers identified 355 genes that it probably possessed. Examining these genes led the researchers to conclude that LUCA would have thrived around vents, where hot water rich in hydrogen, carbon dioxide and minerals could have provided it with the chemicals it needed.

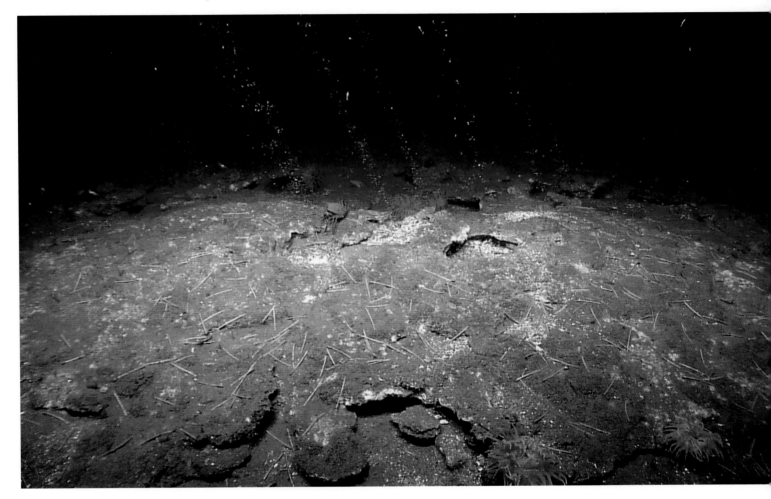

Above: *A cold seep, where water containing hydrocarbon-rich chemicals from petroleum deposits emerges from the seafloor.*

Almost all living cells pump ions across a membrane to produce an electrochemical gradient, then use the gradient to make an energy-rich molecule called adenosine triphosphate. The scientists concluded that, instead of making such a gradient, LUCA could have drawn energy from the natural gradient existing between hydrothermal vent water and seawater. Eventually, early life evolved to be able to generate its own gradient, which would have enabled it to break away from the vent ecosystem. Evidence suggests this happened on at least two occasions, giving rise to the single-celled organisms archaea and bacteria. These primitive life forms subsequently evolved to more complex organisms.

TECHNOLOGICAL ADVANCES PROVIDE A WEALTH OF NEW DATA

Oceanographers gain a new viewpoint in space

When humans ventured into space on the Mercury, Gemini and Apollo missions in the 1960s and early 1970s, they took many photographs of Earth from afar. These revealed features of the oceans, hinting at the possibility of gathering information about the world's oceans from space. As early as 1964, the first conference to discuss this possibility took place at the Woods Hole Oceanographic Institution in Massachusetts, USA. In the preface to the report from the *Oceanography from Space* event, its organizer Gifford Ewing wrote:

> *Intuition tells us that future generations of investigators scanning the oceans from a new vantage point will have the imagination to ask new questions of it and the ingenuity to devise new ways of answering them. It is unthinkable that oceanographers will not find ways to exploit this burgeoning technology for the advancement of their science.*

Two further conferences held in the late 1960s and early 1970s identified ocean data requirements that space technology could potentially help to fulfil. These included determining surface currents; Earth and ocean tides; the shape of the marine geoid (the model of global mean sea level); wind velocity; patterns of wave refraction (the bending of the path of a wave) and spectra (the distribution of wave energy); and wave height. The meetings helped to justify the application of space hardware to oceanography, and to steer the development of appropriate national programmes.

Above: *The Indian Ocean observed from a Gemini spacecraft in the 1960s.*

Among early ocean-viewing satellites were NASA's Skylab and GEOS-3 (Geodynamics Experimental Ocean Satellite), launched in 1973 and 1975 respectively. Skylab's altimeter (a sensor used to determine altitude above a fixed level) successfully observed an anomaly to the geoid caused by the Puerto Rico Trench. And the US National Weather Service of the United States received from GEOS-3 wave height measurements that were accurate enough to be included in its Marine Waves Forecast. Meanwhile, meteorological satellites of NASA's TIROS (Television Infrared Observation Satellite) programme helped to pave the way for accurate sea-surface temperatures from infrared sensors. Experiments were also undertaken around this time to determine if ocean colour might be used as a means to determine sediment and chlorophyll concentrations in seawater.

Right: *NASA's Skylab satellite was one of the first to be used to view the ocean from space.*
Below: *The emergence of satellite technology enabled scientists to observe everything from wave height to sea surface temperature and sediment thickness (seen here).*

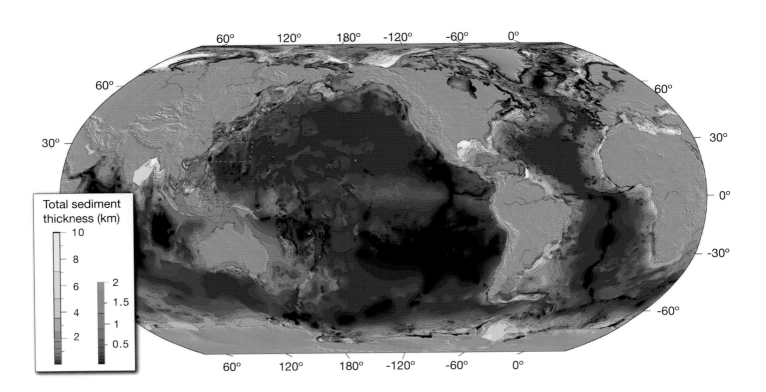

Total sediment thickness (km)

The United States launched a second generation of satellites in the late 1970s: Seasat, the first dedicated oceanography satellite; TIROS-N, aimed at providing high-resolution day and night environmental data; and Nimbus 7, for sensing and collecting atmospheric and ocean colour data. Their onboard instruments measured the marine geoid to a few metres' accuracy; provided data on oceanic surface wind velocities and atmospheric water content; and, thanks to the first ever space-borne 'synthetic aperture radar', penetrated clouds to show sea-surface features, such as surface and internal waves, current boundaries, upwellings and rainfall patterns. Although Seasat remained operational for only 99 days, all the missions were considered to have been highly successful and laid the foundations for future advances in ocean-sensing satellite technology.

Right: *The TIROS-N satellite was launched in the 1970s to gather environmental information.*

Today, numerous satellites operated by agencies around the world enable scientists to conduct a wide range of environment-monitoring programmes. Sensors collect data by detecting energy reflected back from the planet's surface. They can be passive or active. Passive sensors record natural energy, such as sunlight, emitted or reflected back from the Earth's surface. Active sensors use an internal energy source; for example, radar instruments emit a radio wave and measure the time taken for this energy to reflect back from the Earth on to the sensor.

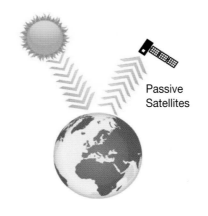

Passive Satellites

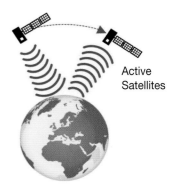

Active Satellites

Sensors operating in different parts of the electromagnetic spectrum provide differing monitoring capabilities. These facilitate cost-effective data gathering on scales from local to global, including areas that would otherwise be very difficult to reach. Among the data gathered today from observing the oceans are: sea-surface temperature, ocean colour, surface winds, wave height and spectra, surface topography and salinity. These are valuable in a wide range of applications from weather forecasting to modelling climate change and identifying the best routes for shipping.

Below: *Satellite image showing the heat reflected off Earth's surfaces in the northeastern USA, with white and blue areas being the coldest and yellow regions the hottest.*

NOAA/NASA

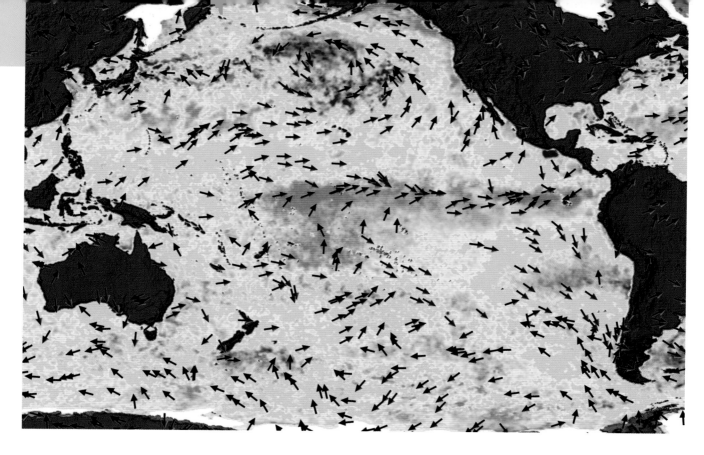

Above: *Satellite image from the 2002–03 El Niño weather cycle showing anomalies in sea-surface temperature in the Pacific Ocean. Areas that are hotter than normal appear orange; those that are cooler than usual are blue. Arrows indicate wind direction.*

Below: *This green chorolphyll bloom is clearly seen from the air.*

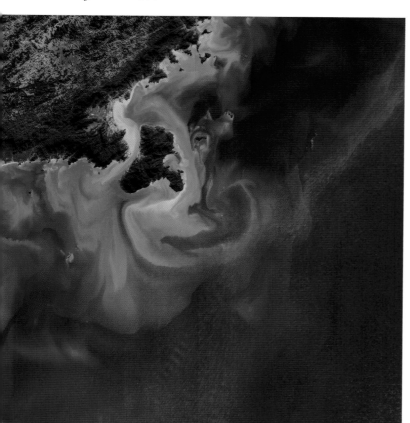

For example, scientists are able to create series of maps from satellite data showing how sea-surface temperature changes over time in different regions. These are helpful for identifying the onset of weather phenomena such as El Niño and La Niña; other climate and weather monitoring and forecasting; validating models showing atmospheric conditions; evaluating coral bleaching episodes caused by elevated seawater temperatures; and managing fisheries. Sea-surface temperature maps can also highlight patterns of water circulation, such as regions of upwelling, where cold waters rise up from the depths, and warm currents, including the Gulf Stream.

Ocean colour observations from satellites, meanwhile, can indicate concentrations of chlorophyll (green photosynthetic pigment found in plants, algae and cyanobacteria). Chlorophyll concentrations in the ocean are an indicator of phytoplankton. These microalgae convert carbon dioxide into oxygen, providing around half of the oxygen we breathe. Monitoring phytoplankton is therefore important for climate, carbon cycle and Earth system studies. Phytoplankton are the basis of the marine food chain, so understanding where concentrations occur is also valuable for fisheries and aquaculture companies. Ocean colour can also indicate where there are blooms of harmful algae.

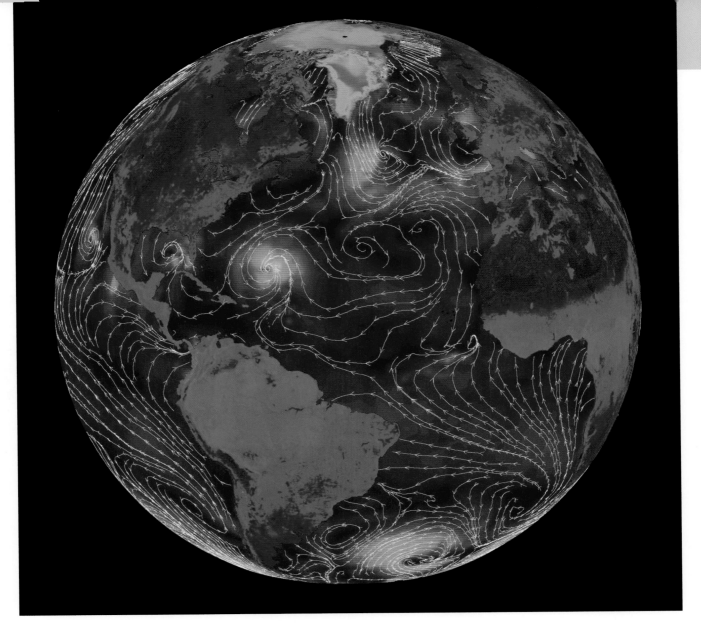

Above: *False-colour image showing wind speeds and directions. Orange highlights the fastest speeds and blue the slowest. White lines indicate direction.*

The sea's surface is the interface between water and air, where moisture and energy are exchanged. Scientists also use satellite observations to learn more about how winds and waves affect the ocean-atmosphere exchanges that underpin global climate. Monitoring winds together with wave height and spectra is also vital for forecasting storms and sea-state conditions, for applications in offshore operations, ship navigation, fisheries and coastal management. With climate change advancing, assessing change over time is a highly valuable use of satellite imaging. Analysis of data from 31 satellites in 2019 found that extreme winds and waves have increased globally over the past three decades, with changes most pronounced in the Southern Ocean.

The half-century since the *Oceanography from Space* conference has confirmed Gifford Ewing's outlook to be correct; the development of satellite technology has revolutionized how we study oceans. However, a limitation is that satellite observing sensors cannot penetrate very far into the ocean itself. This means that observations are limited to the surface or very near surface of the water. Combining satellite data with in situ measurements is helping scientists construct a more comprehensive view of the world's oceans, as the next section shows.

Map of sea surface reveals mountains of the deep

The most accurate global map depicting the ocean floor was produced in 2019 from satellite data of the ocean's surface. Scientists at the USA's Scripps Institution of Oceanography updated earlier efforts using data from the French-Indian satellite-based sensor AltiKa. This is able to measure the distance from the satellite to the sea surface to within 21 mm (0.83 in).

Correcting the data for wave heights and tides revealed the topography of the ocean's surface. Because mountains and troughs on the ocean floor exert a greater or lesser gravitational pull on the water around them, such features cause bumps and gullies on the surface. These were revealed in the satellite data.

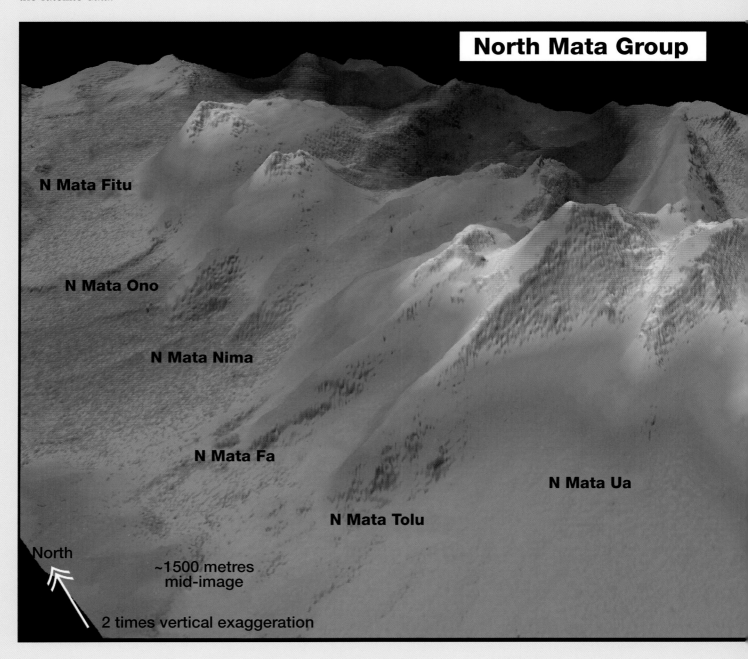

Below: *The ocean floor is punctuated by seamounts, many of which have yet to be investigated.*

The exercise uncovered thousands of previously uncharted underwater mountains; it revealed all such seamounts more than 1.5 km (0.9 miles) tall. The previous most accurate gravity map, produced in 2014, showed only seamounts over 2 km (1.2 miles) tall. However, once Nasa launches its planned SWOT (Surface Water and Ocean Topography) satellite in 2021, it should be possible to use sea-surface mapping to depict all seamounts more than 1 km (0.6 miles) tall.

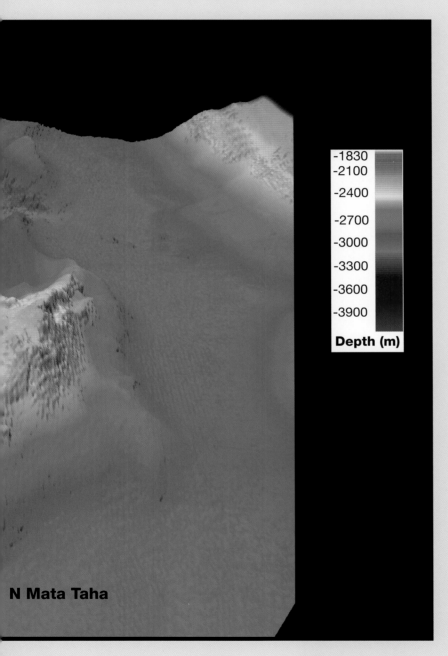

-1830
-2100
-2400
-2700
-3000
-3300
-3600
-3900

Depth (m)

N Mata Taha

Floating robots capture data from beneath the waves

By the late 1990s, scientists were aware that the oceans and atmosphere interacted in complex ways to control the global climate. With rising concern about climate change due to human activities elevating levels of greenhouse gases in the atmosphere, having the means to make systematic global observations of the ocean was becoming critical. Satellite technology had made possible accurate observations of sea-surface features globally and in real time. But scientists lacked the ability to gather data in a similar manner from beneath the waves.

In 1998, a small group of oceanographers suggested that, with sufficient international cooperation, existing technology could be adapted to create a global array of autonomous data-gathering floats. These would supply real-time global views of the oceans that would complement, and help interpret, the satellite-derived datasets. By 2007, 3,000 floats were operational; a decade later, that had risen to 3,800. Today, 26 countries are involved in deploying such floats – known as Argo floats – and processing data from them, with several more contributing logistical support and ship access.

The cylindrical floats are about 150 cm (59 inches) long and powered by batteries that last for five years. Once at sea, they drop through the water column to a depth of 1 km (0.6 miles) and drift with the currents for 10 days. They then sink for a further 1 km before slowly returning to the surface, taking temperature and salinity (saltiness) readings as they go. At the surface, they transmit their data in real-time via satellite to onshore computers. In 2018, an Argo operating in the Atlantic Ocean sent back the programme's 2 millionth profile.

Argo data is freely available for anyone to use, with potential applications ranging from aquaculture to weather forecasting and education. So far, the data has been associated with more than 2,800 publications, with a primary use being to monitor climate variability. One study used Argo data in conjunction with measurements taken during the HMS *Challenger* expedition of 1872 to 1876. This revealed an average warming of 0.3°C over the upper 900 m (2,950 ft) of much of the world ocean during the 135-year study period.

Meanwhile, a study comparing Argo data from 2004 to 2008 with ship-based observations suggested that most regions of the world ocean are warmer in the near surface layer than in previous decades, by over 1°C in some places. Overall, the upper ocean has warmed by 0.2°C globally since the middle of the twentieth century, and other studies indicate further warming at least through to 2013.

Since 1955, the ocean has stored more than 90 per cent of the excess heat trapped by greenhouse gases, acting as a buffer against climate change and shielding us from even higher temperatures. This means that only a small

portion of the additional thermal energy has been involved with melting ice and warming Earth's landmasses; and only a fraction has heated the atmosphere. Therefore – despite what recent abnormally hot weather in parts of Europe may seem to indicate – we are currently experiencing only a miniscule impact from the true warming cost of humanity's use of fossil fuels.

However, the oceans are undergoing changes as a result of the excess heat and additional CO_2 absorbed from the atmosphere. The Fifth Assessment Report published in 2013 by the Intergovernmental Panel on Climate Change concluded that the extra heat has led to 'stratification' where water fails to mix because of differing properties of water masses; changes in ocean current regimes; and the expansion of depleted oxygen zones. And increased levels of CO_2 are making the oceans more acidic, leaving many marine species and ecosystems more vulnerable; increased acidity can prevent some organisms from building shells

Left: *Scientists deploy an Argo float*

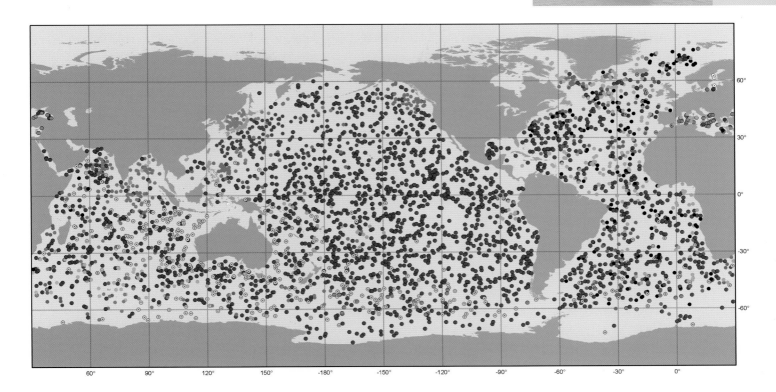

Above: *Map showing Argo floats operational in February 2018. The colours represent the different countries and regions owning the floats.*

and skeletal structures. Weather patterns are changing, too, with extreme events becoming more frequent.

Many questions regarding climate change remain unanswered, however. Oceanographers want to know exactly where the oceans have warmed, by how much, how quickly the warming occurred and, critically, how much heat and CO_2 the ocean will absorb in the future as climate change progresses. To help find answers, there are plans to expand the areas populated by Argo floats, including into regions with seasonal sea-ice. And tests are under way of new types of floats that can take a wider range of measurements and profile the ocean from greater depths.

One of the proposed new profilers contains biogeochemical sensors that can gather data on variables such as oxygen, pH and nitrates. This will enable Argo scientists to analyze effects such as ocean acidification, deoxygenation and the health of marine ecosystems. The average ocean depth is 4,000 m (13,120 ft), so current Argo floats profile only the top half of the water column. A new deep-water float being piloted will extend the vertical range to 6,000 m (19,685 ft). This will enable scientists to study, for example, full-depth ocean circulation. Current systems such as the Atlantic meridional overturning circulation (AMOC), of which the Gulf Stream is a part, are critical for distributing heat, salt, carbon and other nutrients around the planet.

Science writer Justin Gillis of the *New York Times* described Argo as 'one of the scientific triumphs of the age'. Long-term international collaboration and the free sharing of data have contributed to making Argo a success. Given continued goodwill and sufficient funding, further technological advances have the potential to increase the programme's scientific value in future. The hope is that it will continue, for many years to come, to play a key role in helping scientists to map how human activities are changing natural systems and to identify actions that can help minimize harmful impacts.

STUDIES REVEAL LITTLE KNOWLEDGE BUT LARGE IMPACT ON OCEANS

Two major studies published in the first decade of the new millennium highlighted the need to better understand and take care of our oceans. The first, the Census of Marine Life, revealed just how little we know about what lives in the oceans. Involving 2,700 scientists from more than 80 countries, the ten-year project discovered more than 6,000 potentially new species. Among these were a giant species of spiny lobster, *Panulirus barbarae*, located off Madagascar; the shrimp *Neoglyphea neocaledonica*, thought to have gone extinct 50 million years ago but found alive and well in Australia's Coral Sea; and the 'hairy' yeti crab *Kiwa hirsuta*, so unusual that scientists created a new family, Kiwaidae, after finding it near Easter Island. The project found that rare species are common in the oceans.

The study revealed the great diversity of the oceans, increasing the best estimate of the number of known marine species from 230,000 to 250,000. It found life existing under all kinds of conditions, even in extremes of hot and cold, and where light and oxygen were absent. The scientists used genetic barcoding to help untangle the relationships between these diverse life forms. They also looked at how life is distributed throughout the oceans. This work showed that the tropical Western Pacific has the highest diversity of coastal species, and that open-ocean species were concentrated at mid-latitudes across all the oceans. Tellingly, the Census also uncovered the 'unknown unknowns', finding that no records exist for a fifth of the world ocean's volume.

The scientists used records of sightings, catches and even restaurant menus to generate historical baselines of population sizes for different species. Using these to assess changes in the recent past, they documented declining numbers and sizes of certain species, as well as some instances of recovery. They found that phytoplankton, those vital microorganisms at the base of the food chain which help to supply us with oxygen, have declined globally. The team was able to calculate that, by weight, up to 90 per cent of marine life is microbial. However, they also found that knowledge is generally inversely related to size, and that we know much less about these tiny ocean dwellers than we do about larger creatures. Despite all the work, a reliable estimate of the total number of species inhabiting the oceans eluded the team. Their best guess, from extrapolation, was that there are a million species out there, and tens or hundreds of millions of microbes.

As the Census of Marine Life scientists were in the final years of their study, the second project revealed the

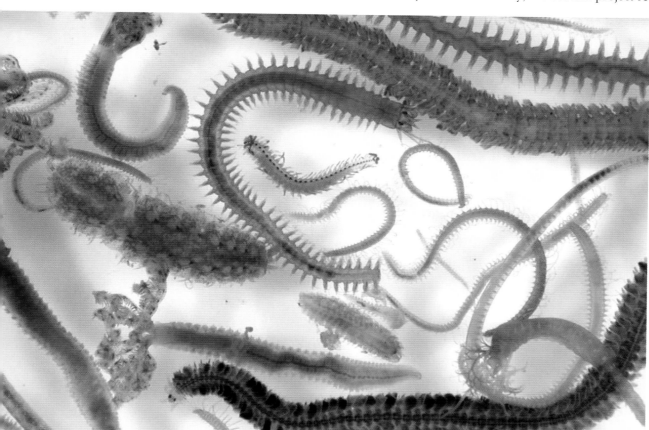

Left: *The Census of Marine Life found a great diversity of species, including many that were new to science.*

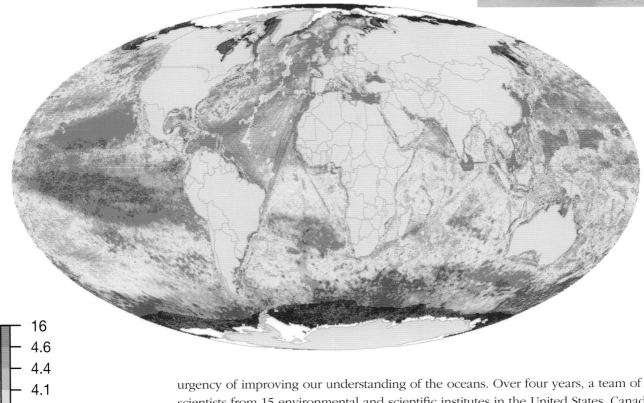

16
4.6
4.4
4.1
3.9
3.8
3.6
3.3
3
2.4
1.8
0
Permanent ice cover
Seasonal ice cover

Above:

Cumulative human impact to marine ecosystems as of 2013. Impact scores are based on 19 stressors; 16 (red) equates to the greatest level of impact, and 0 (blue) to the lowest.

urgency of improving our understanding of the oceans. Over four years, a team of 19 scientists from 15 environmental and scientific institutes in the United States, Canada and the United Kingdom created a global map of the human impact on marine ecosystems. They concluded that human activities have had a strong impact on 41 per cent of the world's oceans, and that as little as 4 per cent of their surface area remained relatively pristine.

The scientists translated human activities into 17 types of impacts, largely related to climate change, fishing and pollution, and then assessed the cumulative impact from these on 20 ecosystems. Guided by expert opinions on how specific human activities affect these different ecosystems, they then calculated cumulative impact scores for each 1 km² cell of ocean to produce the map. The work revealed the North Sea, the South and East China Seas, the Caribbean and North America's East Coast to be most affected by human activities, with less-affected areas mostly located towards the poles. While such impacts had been studied before, the authors claimed the work was the first attempt to synthesize those studies in one database.

With so much of the ocean still to be explored, and so many species as yet unknown, scientists have raised concerns that we could lose potentially useful species before we have even had a chance to document and investigate them. For example, sponges are known to be a good source of bioactive bacteria and could yield useful antibiotics and anti-cancer drugs. Studies such as those outlined above have the potential to help evaluate trade-offs between human uses of the oceans and the protection of ecosystems. The United Nations Sustainable Development Goal 14 aims, among other things, to: 'by 2020 conserve at least ten per cent of coastal and marine areas, consistent with national and international law and based on the best available scientific information'. However, a 2018 study published in *Marine Policy* found that only 3.6 per cent of the ocean was protected in operational Marine Protected Areas (areas of sea that are the equivalent of natural reserves and national parks on land), making reaching this goal unlikely.

Plastic pervades all parts of the oceans

In recent years, the volume of plastics entering the ocean has become a critical issue. Scientists estimate that on average, 8.8 million tons enters the oceans annually (by 2010 figures). It eventually breaks down into tiny microplastic pieces, which can linger in the environment for hundreds of years. One study estimated, in 2014, that more than five trillion plastic pieces weighing more than 250,000 tons were adrift in the ocean. This has severe implications for marine wildlife. An analysis of plastics in the stomachs of fish estimated that as much as 24,000 tons could be being ingested annually from the North Pacific subtropical gyre (a ring-like system of ocean currents forming a vast ecosystem).

In 2019, a 60-year study of plankton was found to have inadvertently charted the rise of plastics in the oceans. The study used a torpedo-shaped marine sampling device towed behind boats to collect plankton, but its operators also recorded when the recorder got tangled up – by what, when and where. This data, captured in hand-written logbooks, shows the rise of plastic pollution from a few strands of fishing twine caught up in 1957, to the appearance of carrier bags from 1965, and more recently, to frequent entanglements by synthetic nets, lines and other fishing equipment.

A 2019 study carried out off California, USA, found plastic at every depth of the ocean. The researchers recorded 2 particles per cubic metre close to the surface, increasing to around 12 particles per cubic metre at depths of around 300 m (985 ft) and then falling again to 2 particles per cubic metre at around 1 km (0.6 miles) below the surface. While more studies are needed to clarify exactly how plastics are distributed in the oceans, a plastic bag was recently documented at a depth of 10,926 m (35,965 ft), down at the bottom of the Mariana Trench, the third time plastic had been recorded in the deepest part of the ocean.

Below:
Plastic is now present across the world's oceans.

PLANS TO REVEAL THE ENTIRE WORLD OCEAN FLOOR BY 2030

'Ocean' is a more appropriate name than 'Earth' for the planet we inhabit, given that oceans cover 71 per cent of its surface. The topography of the seabed is much more pronounced than that of the land, too. The average depth is 3,700 m (12,140 ft), compared to an average height of land of 840 m (2,755 ft). However, despite the immense human effort and technological advances of the past centuries, less than 18 per cent of the ocean floor has been surveyed to a resolution of 1,000 m (0.6 miles). In other words, the maps we have for more than 80 per cent of the oceans only show features that are greater than one kilometre across. Without knowing the detail of the underlying terrain, we risk misinterpreting the myriad studies being conducted between the ocean surface and floor.

Below: *Oceans cover 71 per cent of the world's surface.*

Having a poor understanding of the ocean floor could compromise nations' safety, security and economic health. Why? Because detailed knowledge of seabed bathymetry is critical to understanding ocean circulation patterns, which have a bearing on everything from climate and weather patterns to tsunami formation and human exploration for deep-sea resources. Moreover, the 'blue economy' supports the equivalent of 31 million full-time jobs, provides food to 3 billion people who depend on fish for protein and has great potential to provide renewable energy from waves. And in a world highly dependent on digital communication, we need to understand the

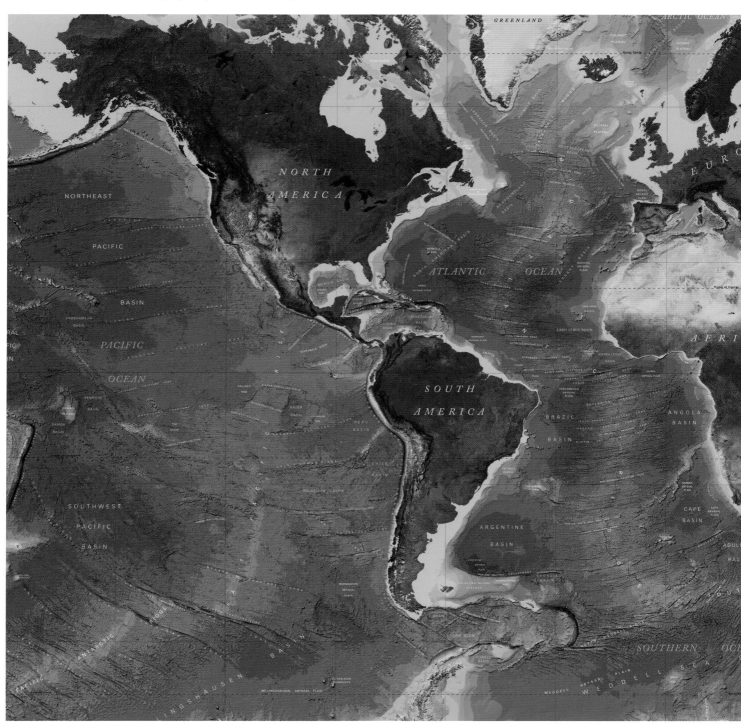

seafloor terrain in order to maintain and add to the extensive array of submarine cables that connect us across the globe.

Since the first edition of the General Bathymetric Chart of the Oceans (GEBCO) was produced in 1903 (see page 145), the GEBCO Guiding Committee has continued to regularly publish updated editions. In 1983, hard copy maps gave way to a digital atlas format, produced on a CD-ROM. Twenty years later, as GEBCO celebrated its 100th anniversary, a centenary edition included the first release of a bathymetric grid, providing ocean depth data on a one-minute global grid. This edition also included 'trackline' information, detailing paths taken by particular surveys to highlight the data used for compiling the map. This showed that that detailed coverage of the ocean floor remained patchy.

On presenting the first edition of GEBCO in 1904, Professor Julien Thoulet had said: 'Here then is everything that is known today about the relief of the ocean floor. For many years to come, mariners, telegraphists, engineers, oceanographers, and scientists will continue their soundings, for now we must proceed to fill in the details; no point of any sea on the globe will escape our investigations.' However, in *The History of GEBCO 1903–2003* the authors concluded that: 'Nearly 100 years on, Professor Thoulet's remarks appeared equally applicable on the release of the Centenary Edition of the GDA.'

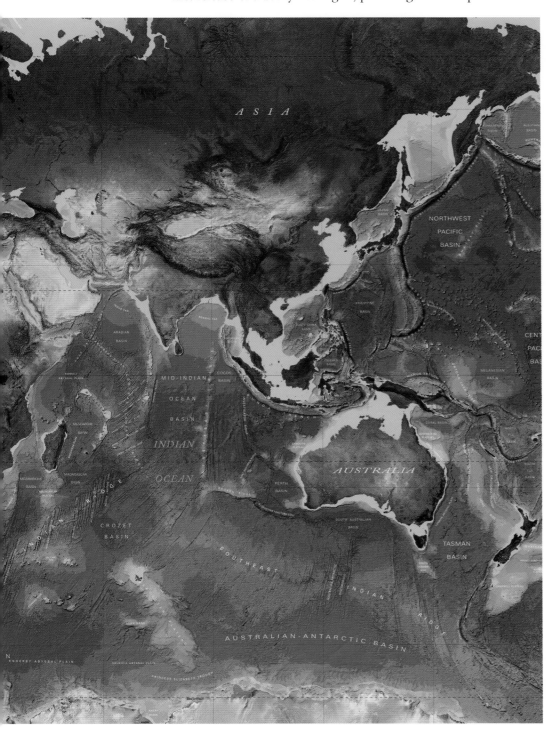

Left: *The 2014 revision of the General Bathymetric Chart of the Oceans.*

Robots key to future ocean mapping

Unmanned robots are likely to be central to future efforts to map the oceans. In an attempt to spur innovation in this field, the Ocean Discovery XPRIZE was launched in 2015. The winner of the main US $4million prize, announced in 2019, was the 16-strong GEBCO-Nippon Foundation Alumni Team. It won the competition – which involved producing a 5 m (16 ft) resolution bathymetric map in 24 hours, and taking multiple images of the seabed – with SeaKIT. SeaKIT comprises an established autonomous underwater vehicle paired with a specially developed un-crewed surface vessel. The team covered 278 km² (107 miles²) within the allotted time period, and took more than ten images of recognizable geological features. The team plans to reinvest the prize money in future ocean-mapping initiatives. SeaKIT is likely to play a role in meeting the goals of the Seabed 2030 Project.

Above: *SeaKIT's Unmanned Surface Vehicle USV Maxlimer.*

It has often been said that we know more about the surface of the Moon, Mars, and Venus than we do about the depths of the ocean. While satellite data enabled scientists to produce the 2019 gravity map (see page 178) reflecting the global topography of the ocean floor, the resolution of this map is only around 6 km. Only 10–15 per cent of the ocean floor has been mapped at 100 m resolution, which is achieved using multibeam sonar systems aboard ships. By comparison, the entire Moon and Martian surfaces, and 98 per cent of the surface of Venus, have been mapped at 100 m resolution.

The disappearance without trace of Malaysia Airlines flight MH370; the loss of marine habitats; natural disasters such as the 2011 Tōhoku earthquake and tsunami in Japan; increasing demand for offshore energy; and expanding commercial exploration of marine resources for potential medicines, minerals and metals have all highlighted the need for better knowledge of the sea floor. Meanwhile, the United Nations Sustainable Development Goal 14 aims to steer a path through these often contradictory drivers to conserve and sustainably use the oceans, seas and marine resources through enhanced scientific knowledge and research capacity.

In 2017, GEBCO partnered with the Nippon Foundation to launch the Seabed 2030 project. This international effort seeks to bring together all available bathymetric data to produce a definitive map of the world ocean floor by 2030 and make it freely available to all. The project was launched at the first-ever United Nations Oceans Conference in June 2017. Later that year, the UN declared 2021–2030 the Decade of Ocean Science for Sustainable Development. The hope is that the Decade will raise awareness of our dependence on the ocean, strengthen international cooperation in scientific research programmes, reduce the risks facing mariners – posed by severe weather such as hurricanes, as well as physical hazards including reefs and sand bars – and improve how we manage vital but vulnerable ocean and coastal environments in the coming centuries.

Left: *The first-ever United Nations Ocean conference took place in 2017.*

Below: *Nekton is using submersibles and drones to learn more about the oceans.*

Pioneering broadcast links people to the underwater world

In 2019, the UK not-for-profit research institute Nekton made history when it broadcast a live TV-quality video transmission wirelessly from a submersible 60 m (197 ft) down in the Indian Ocean. It did so at the start of a seven-week expedition to the Seychelles, where it sought to gather data to support the Seychelles' commitment to protecting 30 per cent of its waters. This was the first in an ambitious programme of expeditions employing crewed submersibles and underwater drones to investigate the Indian Ocean, the world's least explored and least protected ocean.

Supported by more than 40 organizations around the world, Nekton aims to explore and conserve all the world's oceans, with the guiding objective of helping to protect at least 30 per cent of them by 2030. It particularly seeks to explore the water from the surface down to 450 m (1,476 ft), which is highly biodiverse but also highly vulnerable to human activities. By combining scientific research, capacity development programmes, and ocean management and governance initiatives with public outreach, Nekton hopes to engage people and make them aware of just how much we all depend on healthy oceans for our wellbeing.

INDEX

t = top, b = bottom, l = left, r = right

Alamy: 131, 136, 188

Benjamin Halpern: 183

Blue Water Recoveries Ltd: 65t (Peter Holt)

Bridgeman Images: 19, 45b, 47, 59, 67b, 75, 81, 148

British Museum: 17b, 29

Census of Marine Life: 182

David Woodroffe: 10, 21, 141t, 142t

Getty Images: 18, 111t, 111b, 121, 151, 159, 162b, 163, 189t

IODP: 160, 166 (NSF/JRSO/Tim Fulton)

Library of Congress: 15t, 70, 99, 114, 139

Lovell Johns: 26, 55t, 116

Metropolitan Museum of Art: 13b (Rogers Fund, 1980), 17t (Rogers Fund, 1930), 117 (Cyrus W. Field, 1892)

© National Maritime Museum, Greenwich, London: 7, 8, 14, 16, 28, 30, 52, 55b, 60, 61, 63, 64t, 74b, 76, 79, 80, 82, 83t, 84t, 84b, 85, 86, 87, 89t, 89b, 90, 93, 95, 96, 97, 101b, 106, 112, 126, 132, 147

NASA: 157, 158, 172, 176t, 176b, 177

Naval History and Heritage Command: 153t, 155

Nekton Mission: 189b

NOAA: 109, 128, 134, 135t, 135b, 140, 145b, 154, 156, 164, 168t, 168b, 170, 171, 173b, 174, 175, 176b, 178, 180,

Public Domain: 1, 2, 9, 11, 12b (www.deepreef.org), 13t, 15b, 20, 23t, 23b, 24, 25, 27t, 27b, 32, 34, 36, 37t, 37b, 38, 42, 44, 45t, 48, 49, 50, 51, 53, 54, 56, 57, 60b, 62t, 62b, 64b, 65, 67t, 68, 69, 72, 74t, 78t, 78b, 79, 83b, 88, 92, 98, 100, 101t, 102, 104, 105, 108, 110, 113t, 113b, 118, 119t, 120b, 122b, 123, 124b, 125, 127, 137, 141, 142b, 143t, 144, 145, 146b, 149l, 149r, 150b, 152, 153b, 169, 173t, 179b, 181, 182, 183, 185, 186 (GEBCO)

Shutterstock: 12t, 22, 31, 41, 129, 130, 138, 167, 184

Science Photo Library: 143t, 162t, 176t

Wellcome Collection: 120t, 122t, 124t, 143b, 146t, 150t